Simply Gersh

The Music of George & Ira Gershwin®

20 of Their Most Popular Works

Arranged by Tom Gerou

Simply Gershwin is a collection of some of the most beloved songs by George Gershwin (1898–1937) and Ira Gershwin (1896–1983), as well as themes from the famous *Rhapsody in Blue*. These have been carefully selected and arranged by Tom Gerou for Easy Piano, making many of Gershwin's most lyrical melodies and swinging rhythms accessible to pianists of all ages. Phrase markings, articulations, fingering and dynamics have been included to aid with interpretation, and a large print size makes the notation easy to read.

George Gershwin (born Jacob Gershowitz) was born in Brooklyn, New York, and grew up in a musical Russian Jewish immigrant family with three siblings. His brother, Ira, became a lifelong songwriting collaborator and together they produced many of the world's most famous tunes—*I Got Rhythm, Someone to Watch over Me, Embraceable You* and many others. Gershwin's greatest contribution to music was bridging the worlds of classical music, jazz and popular song—drawing upon the textures of French Impressionism, the harmonies and rhythms of Tin Pan Alley, and the folk songs of the deep South to create his unique voice. His songs have been used on television and in films, and have been recorded by countless singers and musicians. For these reasons and more, his music is exciting to explore.

After all, he is *Simply Gershwin!*

GERSHWIN®, GEORGE GERSHWIN® and IRA GERSHWIN™
are registered trademarks of Gershwin Enterprises
RHAPSODY IN BLUE™ is a trademark of the George Gershwin Family Trust
All Rights Reserved

Copyright © MMVII by ALFRED PUBLISHING CO., INC.
All rights reserved. Printed in USA.
ISBN-10: 0-7390-4481-8
ISBN-13: 978-0-7390-4481-0

Contents

Somebody Loves Me

Words by B.G. DeSylva and Ballard MacDonald
Music by George Gershwin
Arranged by Tom Gerou

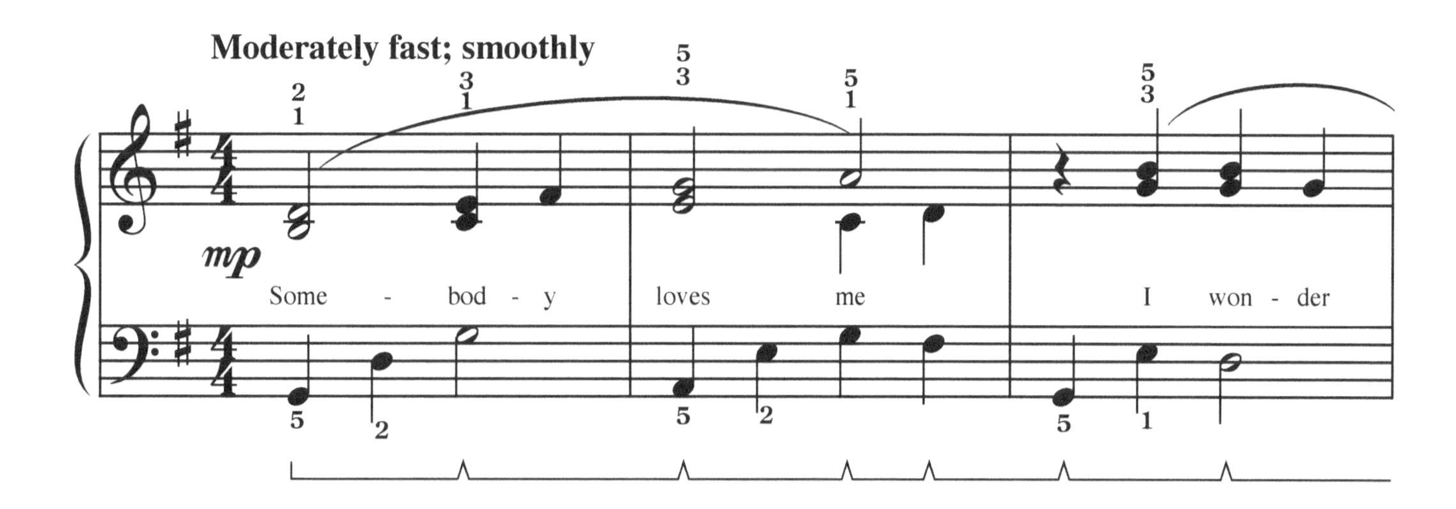

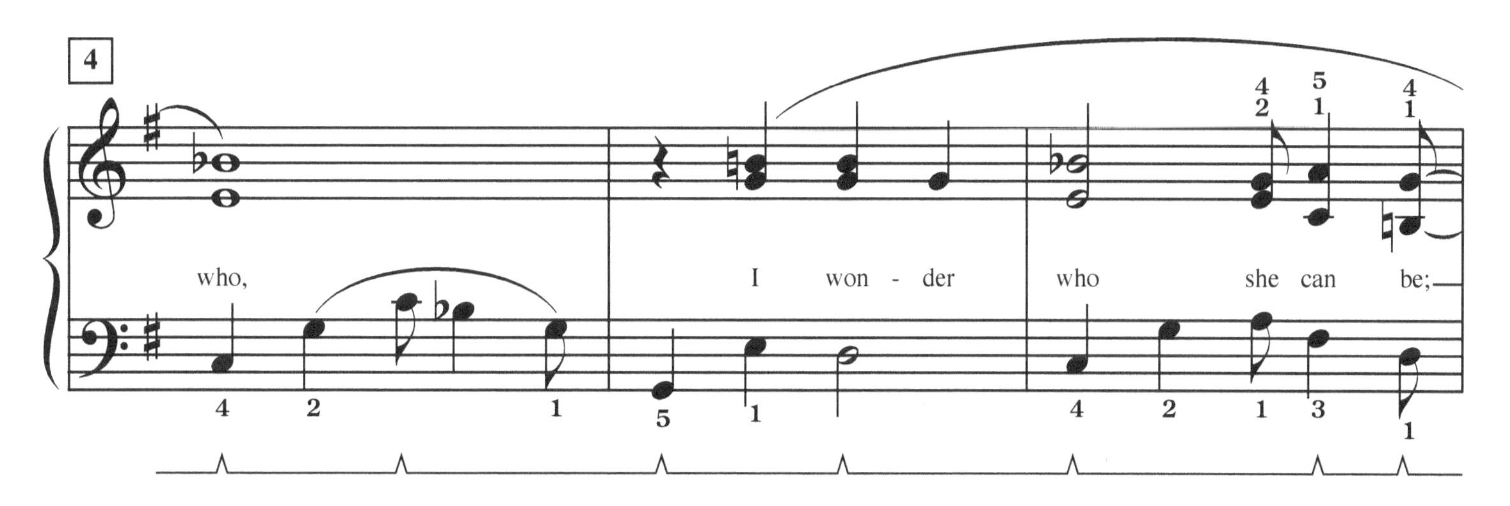

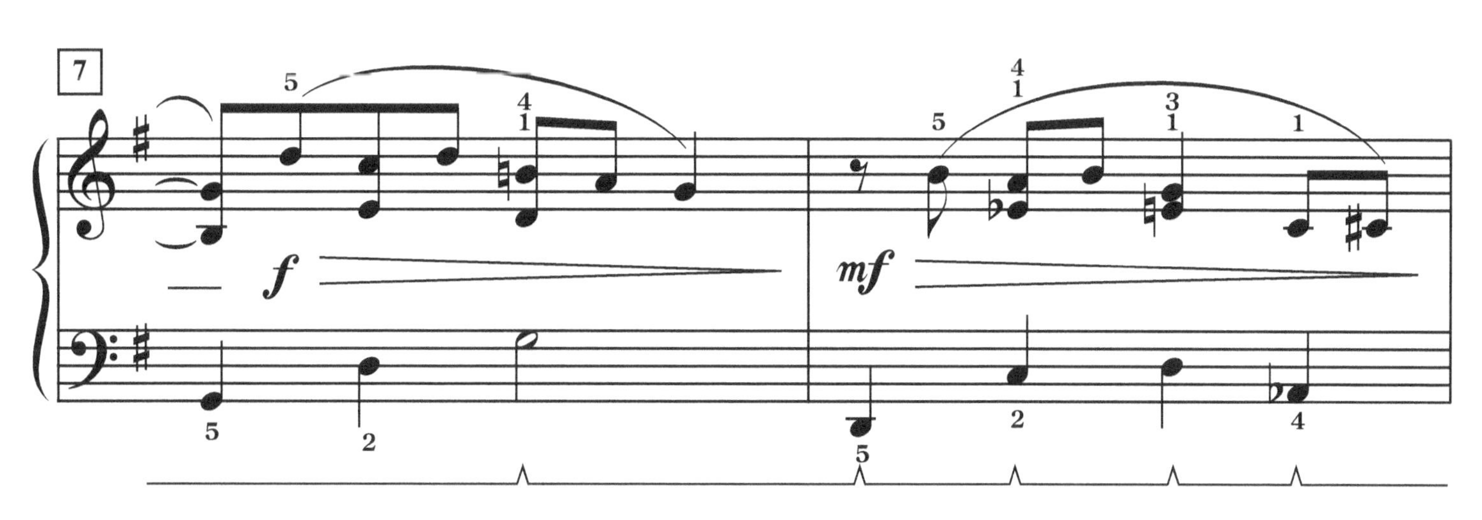

© 1924 (Renewed) WB MUSIC CORP.
All Rights Reserved

9
mp
Some - bod - y loves me I wish I
12
knew,
mf
Who can she be wor - ries me,
15
For ev - 'ry girl who pass - es
18
me I shout, Hey! may - be,

21
You were meant to be my lov - ing ba - by;
24
mp
Some - bod - y loves me
27
I won - der who,
f
May - be it's you.
rit.
30

Bidin' My Time

Music and Lyrics by
George Gershwin and Ira Gershwin
Arranged by Tom Gerou

© 1930 (Renewed) WB MUSIC CORP.
All Rights Reserved

11
mp
Next year,
Next year,
Some - thin's bound to

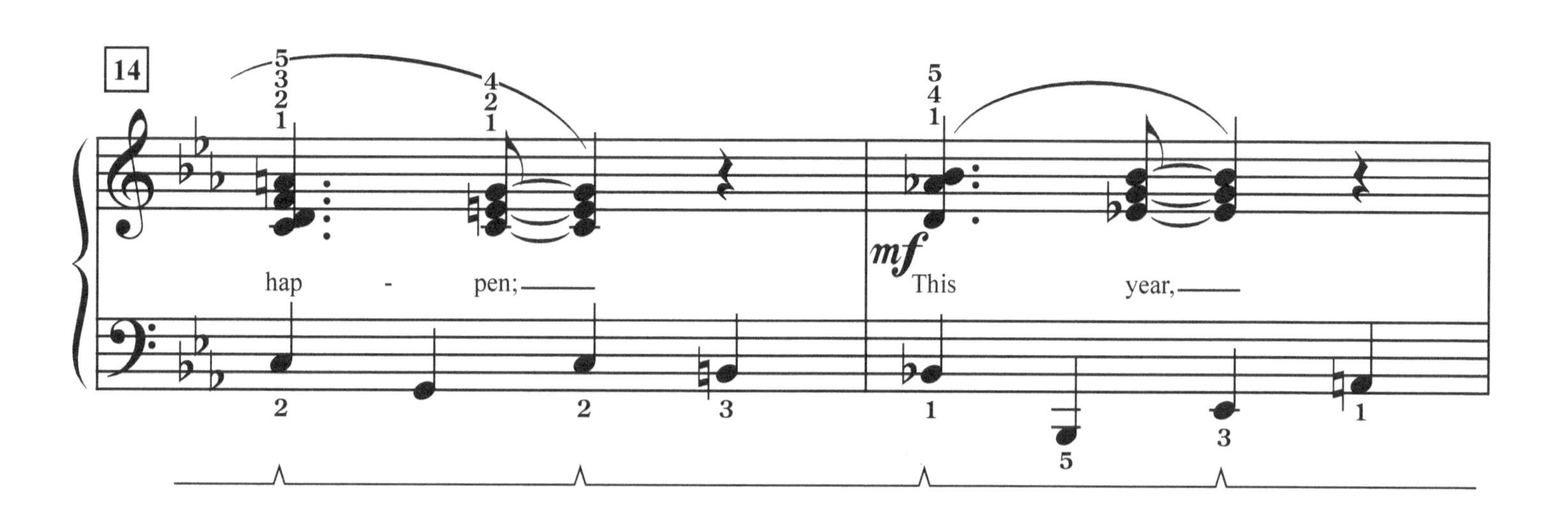
14
hap - pen;
mf
This year,

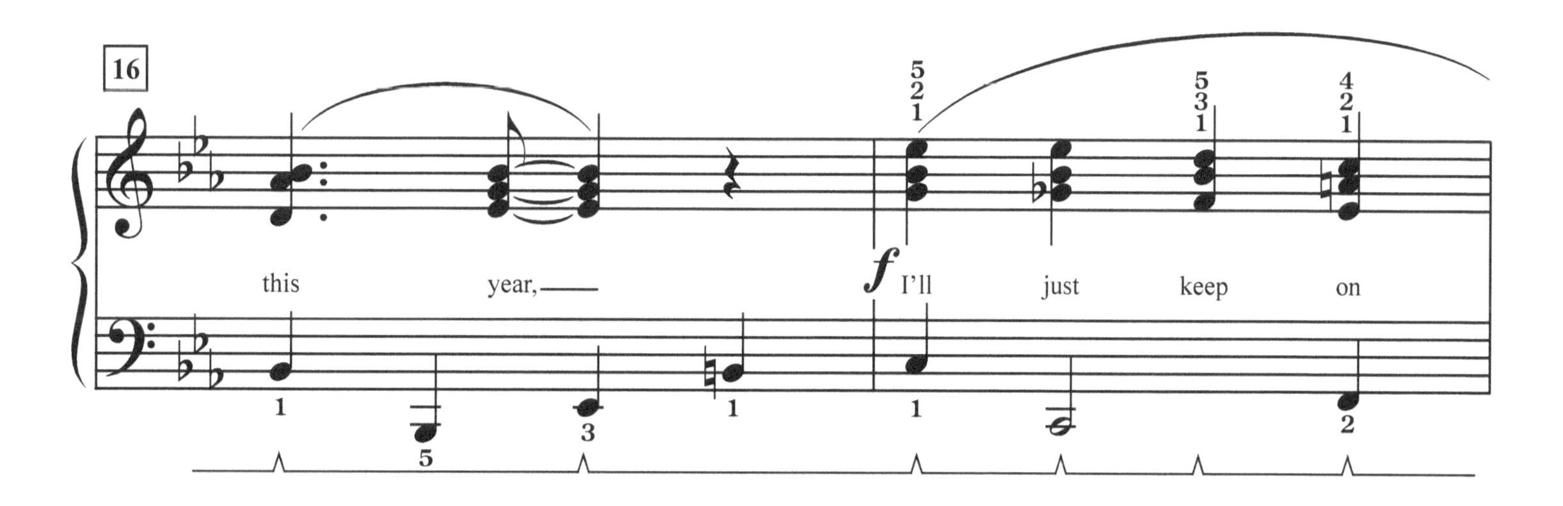
16
this year,
f
I'll just keep on

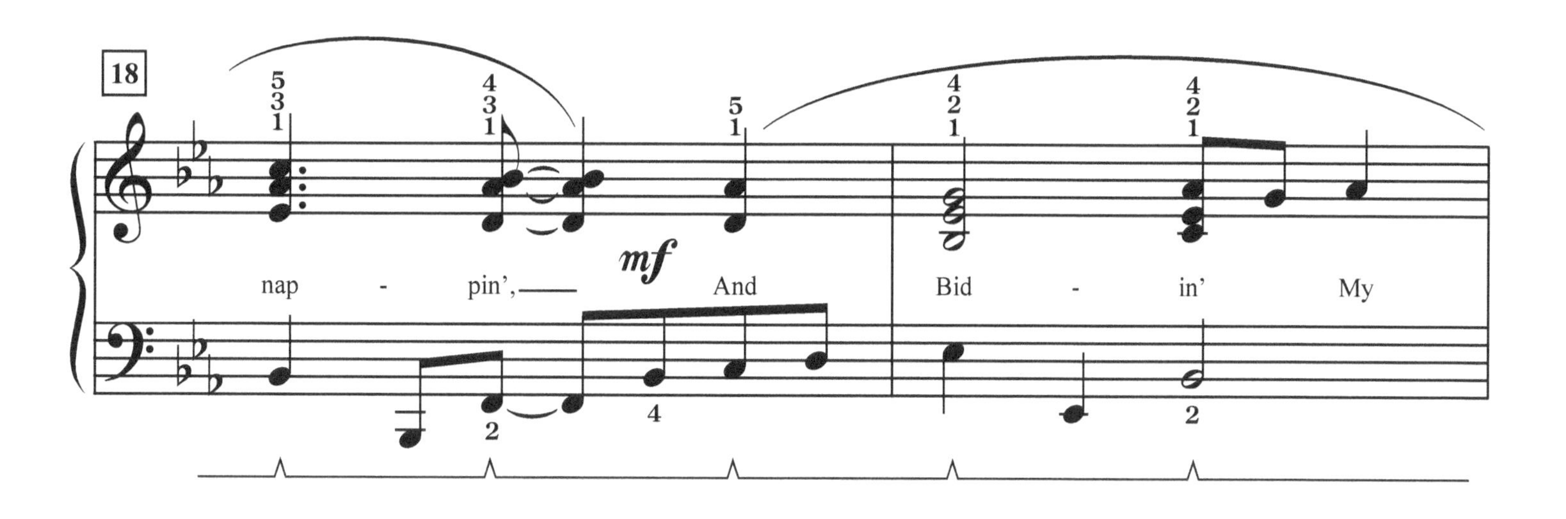
18
nap - pin',
mf
And
Bid - in' My

20
Time 'Cause that's the kind - a guy
22
I'm. There's no re - gret - tin'
f
24
When I'm set - tin' Bid - in' My Time.
mp
cresc.
27
ff

A Foggy Day

Music and Lyrics by
George Gershwin and Ira Gershwin
Arranged by Tom Gerou

© 1937 (Renewed) GEORGE GERSHWIN MUSIC and IRA GERSHWIN MUSIC
All Rights Administered by WB MUSIC CORP.
All Rights Reserved

13
The Brit - ish Mu - se - um had
16
lost its charm.
mp
How long, I won -
19
- dered, could this thing last?
mf
But the
22
age of mir - a - cles had - n't passed,

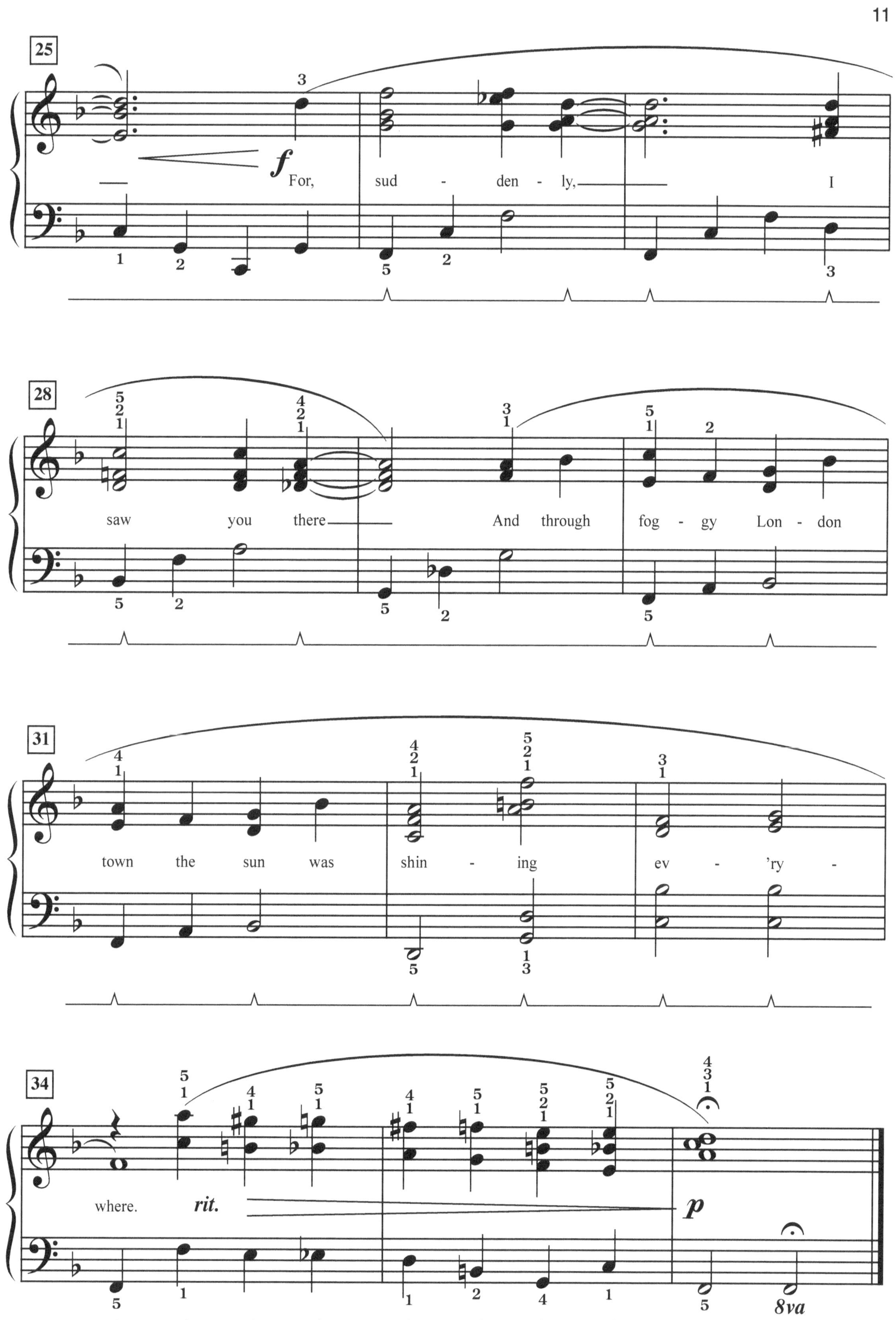

25
For, sud - den - ly, I
28
saw you there And through fog - gy Lon - don
31
town the sun was shin - ing ev - 'ry -
34
where.
rit.
8va

Prelude II

(Blue Lullaby)

(1927)

By George Gershwin

Arranged by Tom Gerou

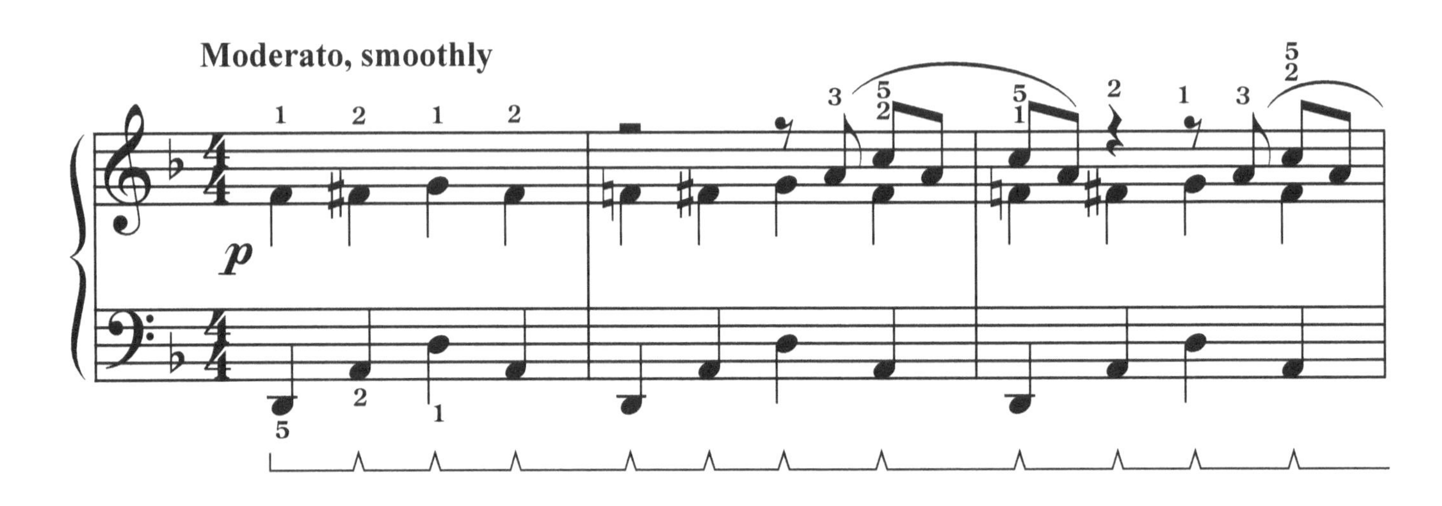

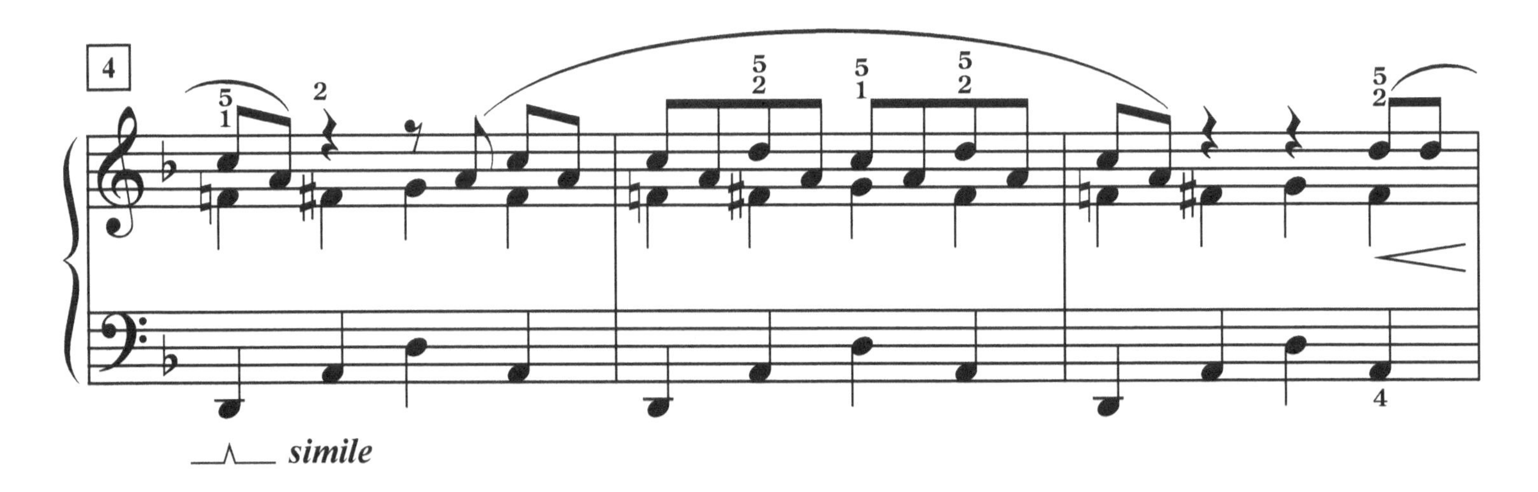

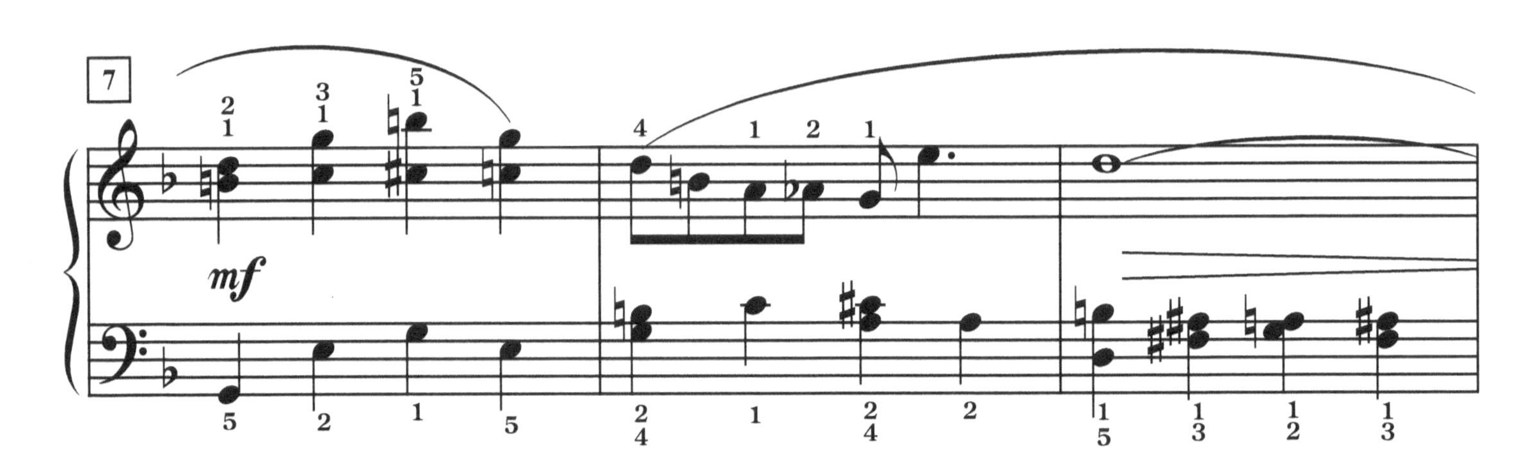

© 1927 (Renewed) WB MUSIC CORP. in the U.S.
Rights throughout the World excluding the U.S. and British Reversionary Territories Controlled by
NEW WORLD MUSIC COMPANY (LTD.) and Administered by WB MUSIC CORP.
Rights throughout the British Reversionary Territories controlled by CHAPPELL & CO.
All Rights Reserved including Public Performance

10
p
13
to Coda
pp
rit.
15
a tempo
p
simile
18

21
mf

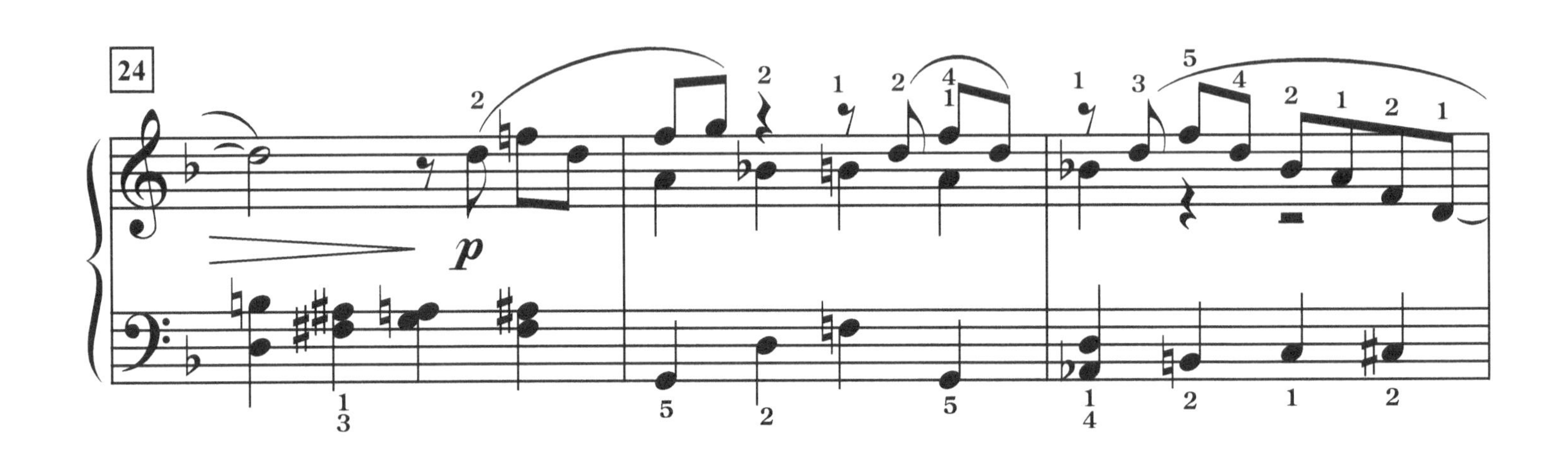
24
p

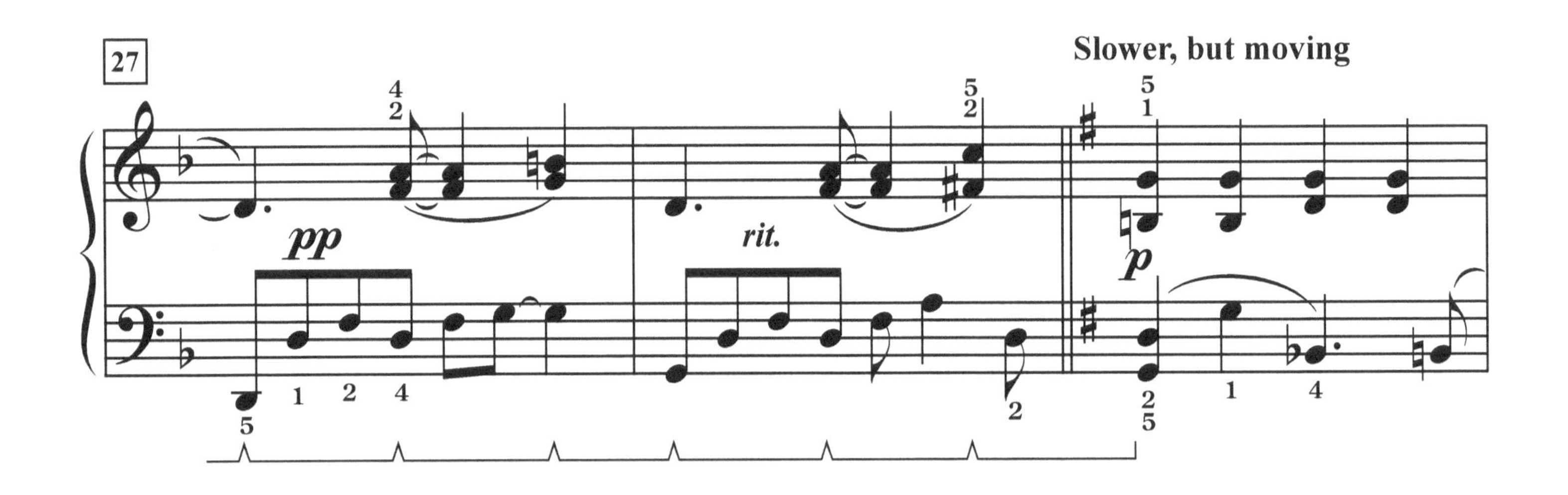
27
Slower, but moving
pp
rit.
p

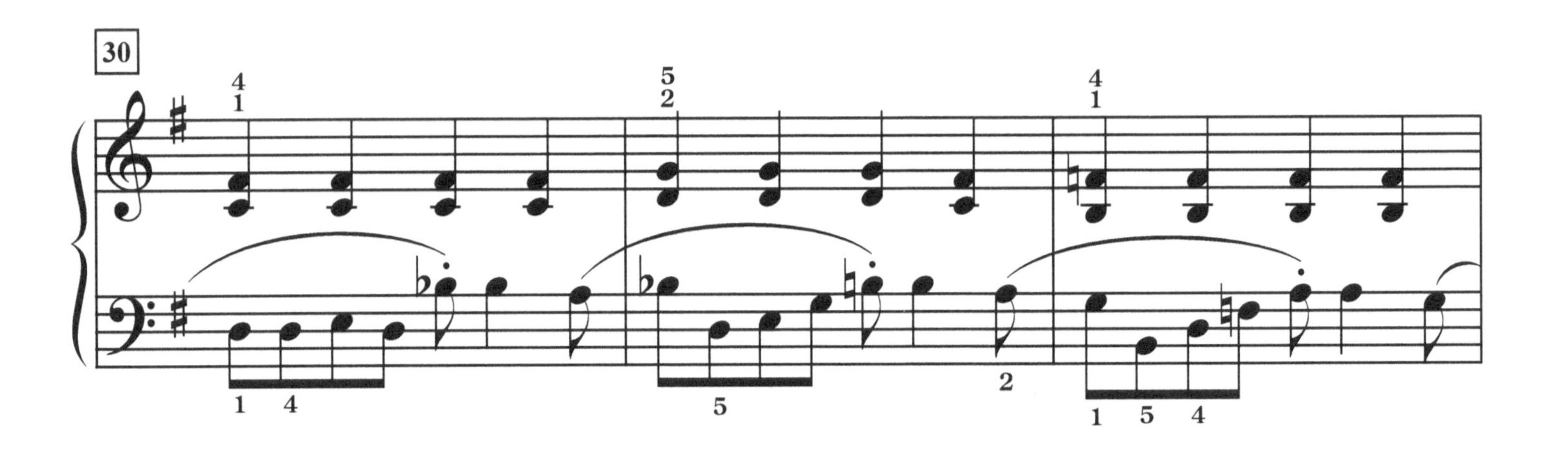
30

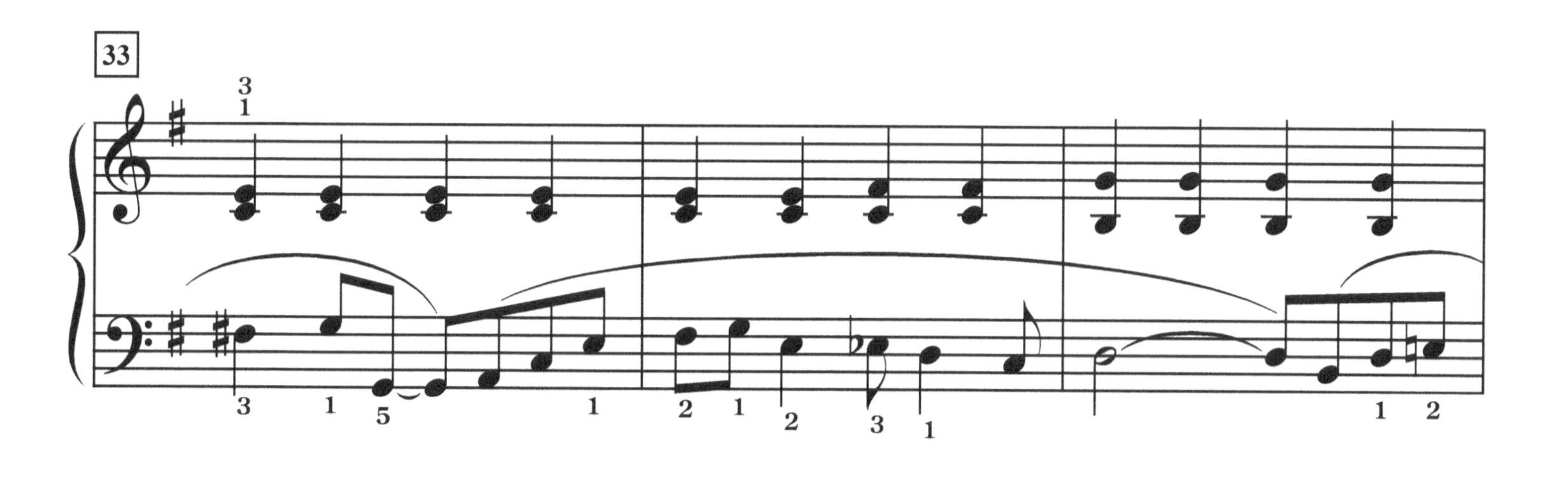
33

36

39
D.C. al Coda
pp
rit.

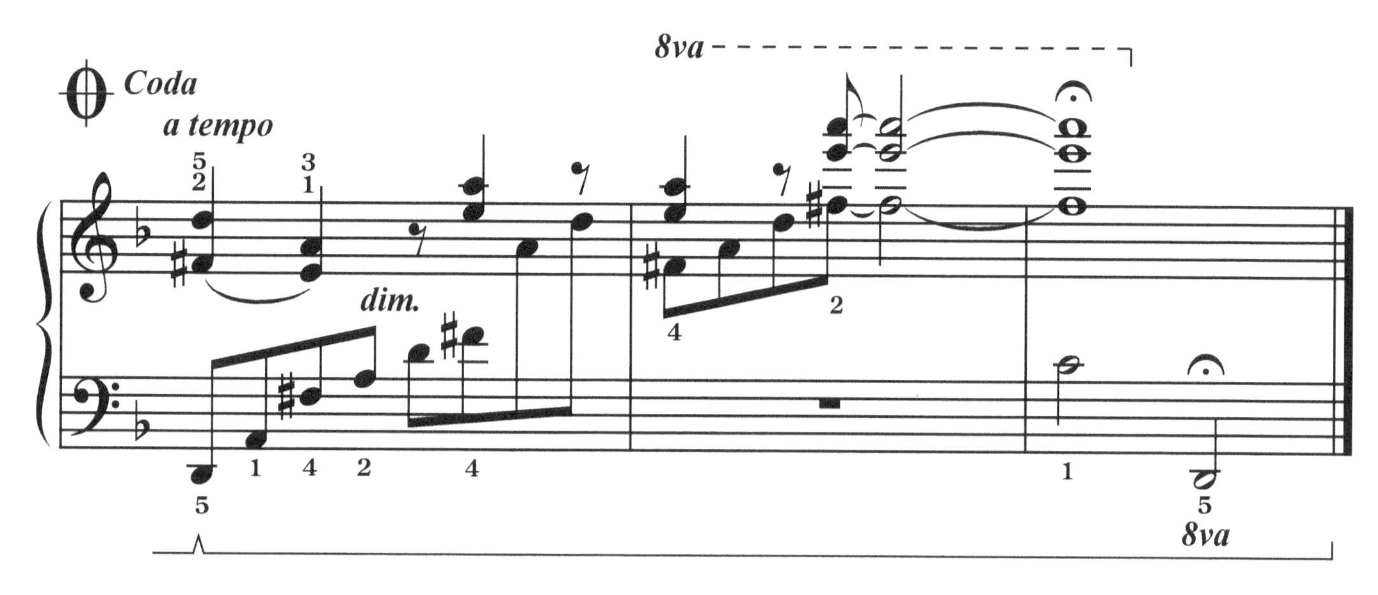
Coda
a tempo
dim.
8va
8va

I Got Rhythm

Music and Lyrics by
George Gershwin and Ira Gershwin
Arranged by Tom Gerou

© 1930 (Renewed) WB MUSIC CORP.
All Rights Reserved

12
pas - tures,
I got
my man Who could
15
ask for an - y - thing
more?
mf
Old Man
18
Trou - ble,
I don't
mind him,
simile
21
You won't
find him
'Round my

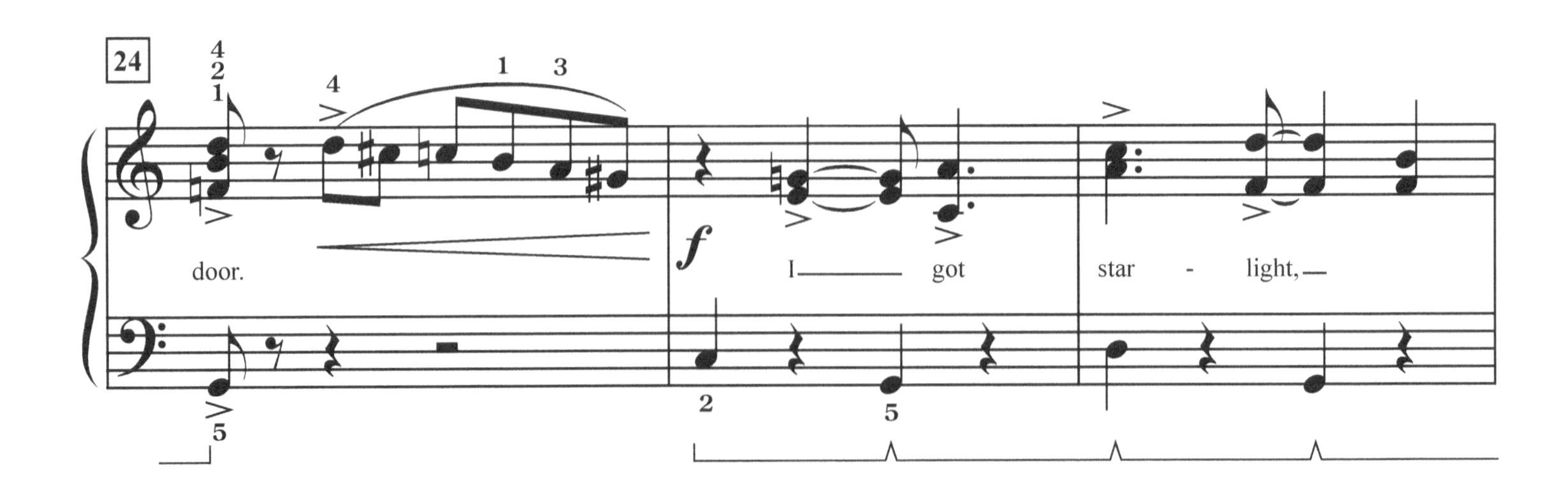
24
door.
f
I got
star - light,
simile

27
I got
sweet dreams,
I got

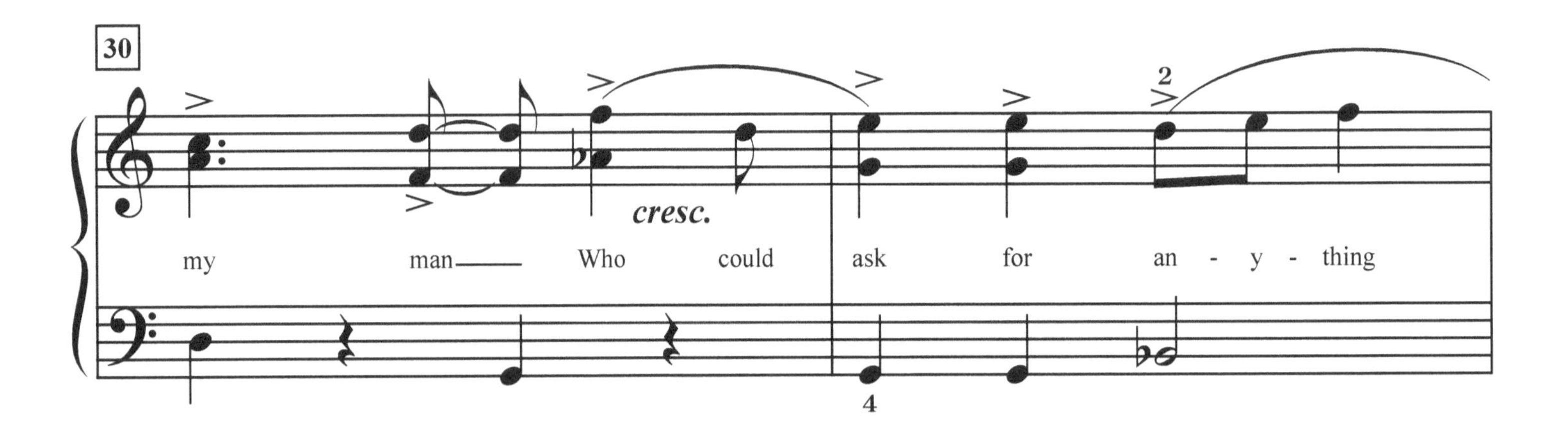
30
my man Who could
cresc.
ask for an - y - thing

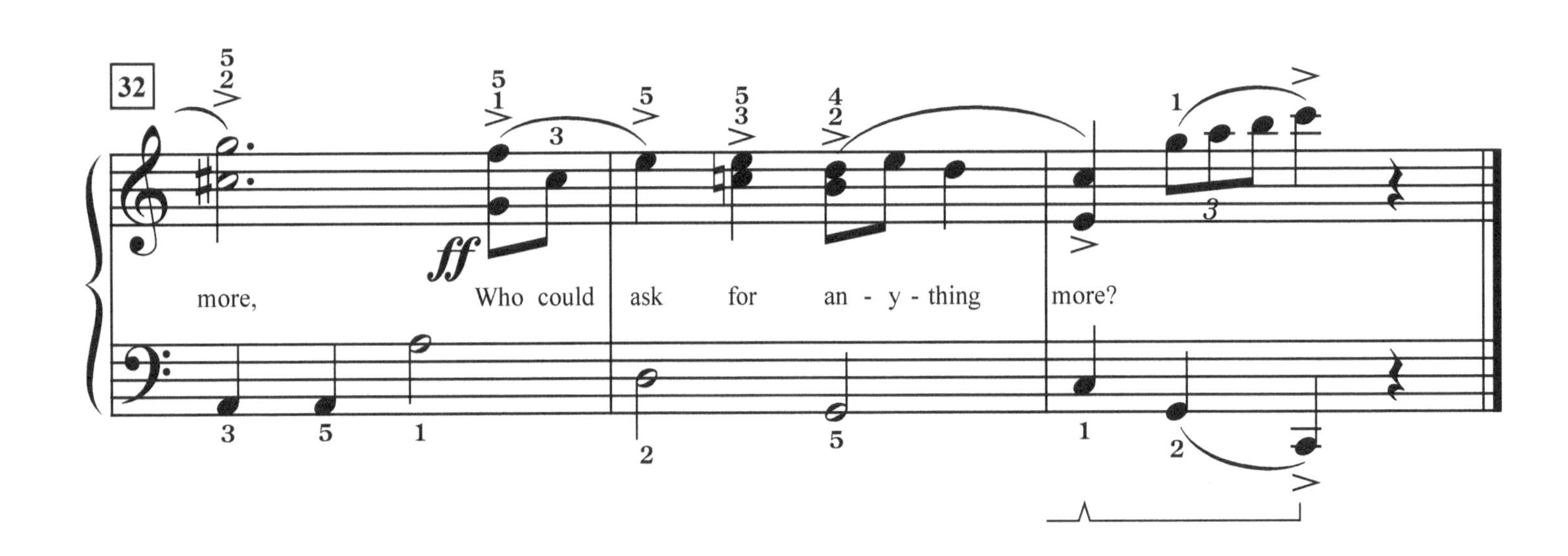
32
more,
ff
Who could
ask for an - y - thing
more?

I've Got a Crush on You

Music and Lyrics by
George Gershwin and Ira Gershwin
Arranged by Tom Gerou

© 1930 (Renewed) WB MUSIC CORP.
All Rights Reserved

10
nev - er had the least no - tion.
13
that I could fall with so much e -
16
mo - tion.
Could you coo,
mp
19
Could you care
simile

22
for a cun - ning
cot - tage
cresc.
we could share?
25
mf
The
world will par - don my mush,
29
'Cause I've got a
f
crush, my ba - by, on
32
you.
1.
I've got a
2.

Let's Call the Whole Thing Off

Music and Lyrics by
George Gershwin and Ira Gershwin
Arranged by Tom Gerou

© 1936, 1937 (Copyrights Renewed) GEORGE GERSHWIN MUSIC and
IRA GERSHWIN MUSIC
All Rights Administered by WB MUSIC CORP.
All Rights Reserved

12
I like to-mah-to; Po - ta - to, Po-tah-to, To - ma - to, To-mah-to!
15
mp
Let's Call the Whole Thing Off! But oh!
18
If we call the whole thing off, Then we must part. And
21
oh! If we ev - er part, Then that might break my

24
heart! So, if you like pa - ja - mas And I like pa - jah - mas,
27
I'll wear pa - ja - mas and give up pa - jah - mas.
For we know we
simile
30
need each oth - er, So we
bet - ter call the call - ing off
32
off.
Let's Call the Whole Thing Off!
8va

Love Is Here to Stay

Music and Lyrics by
George Gershwin and Ira Gershwin
Arranged by Tom Gerou

© 1938 (Renewed) CHAPPELL & CO.
All Rights Reserved

13
tel - e - phone and the mov - ies that we know May just be
16
pass - ing fan - cies, And in time may go.
19
mf
But, oh my dear, Our love is here to
22
stay; To - geth - er we're

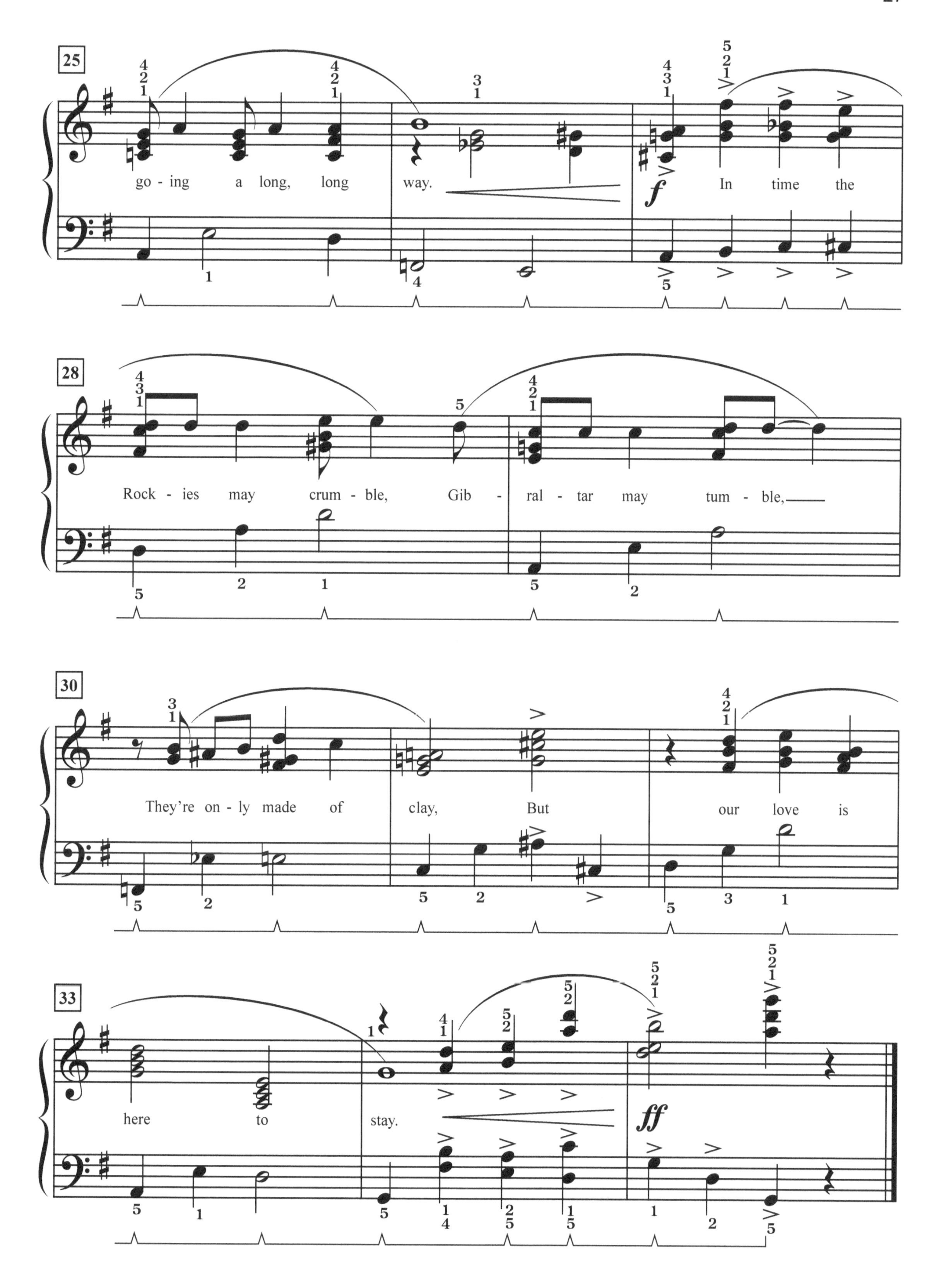
25
going a long, long way.
f
In time the
28
Rockies may crumble, Gibraltar may tumble,
30
They're only made of clay, But our love is
33
here to stay.
ff

Lullaby
(for String Quartet)

By George Gershwin
Arranged by Tom Gerou

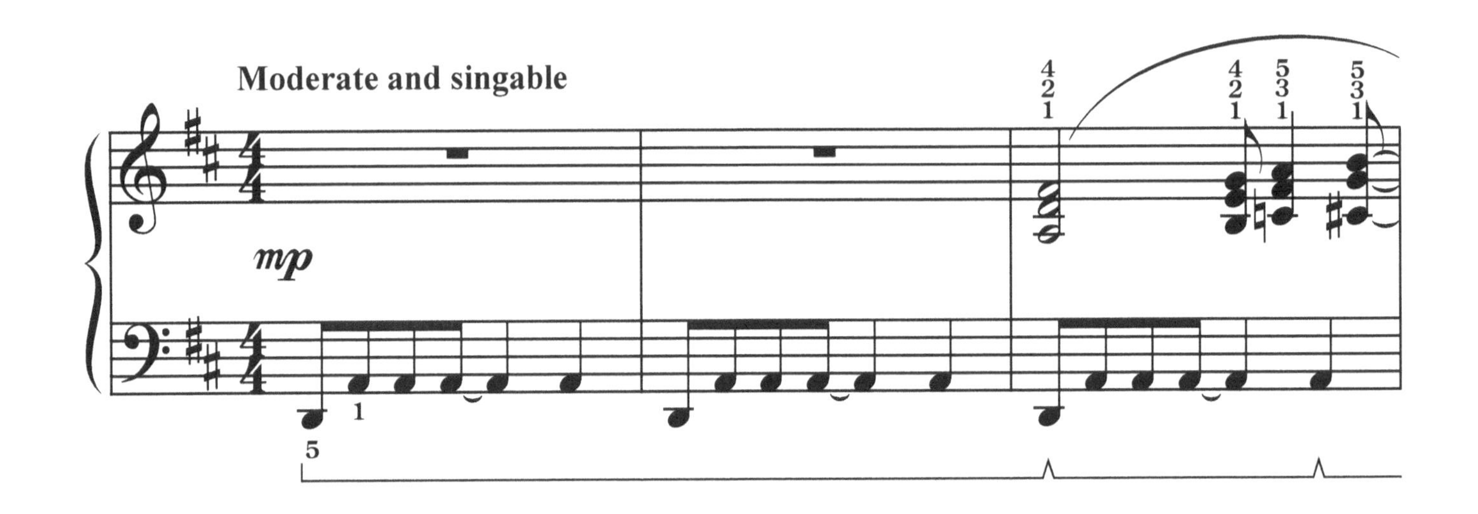

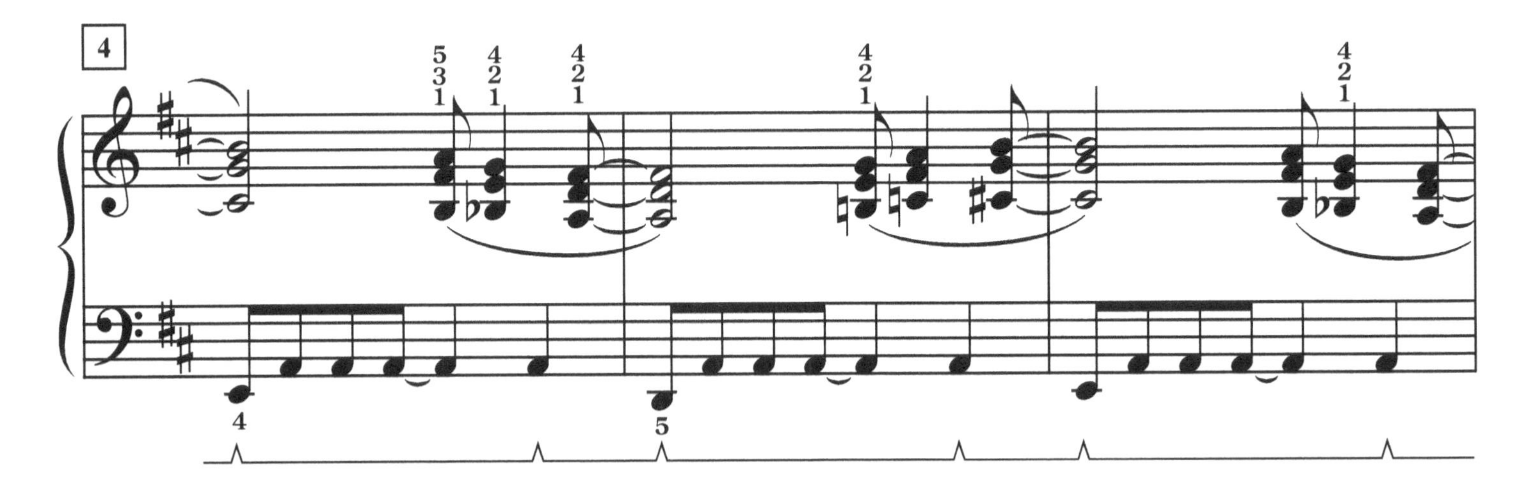

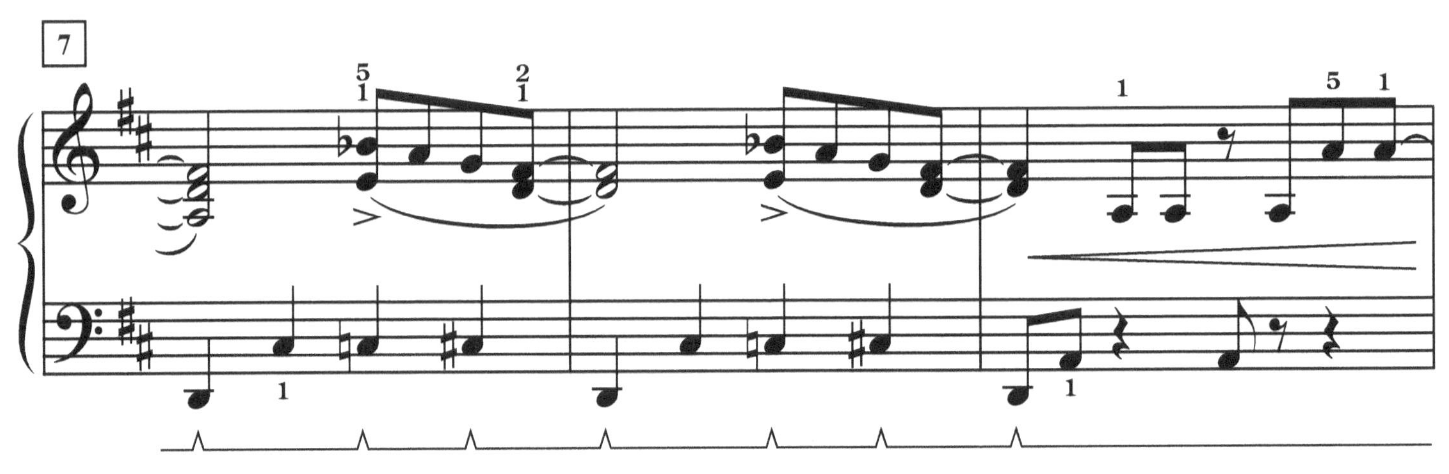

© 1963 (Renewed) GEORGE GERSHWIN MUSIC
All Rights Administered by WB MUSIC CORP.
All Rights Reserved

mf
p
mf
rit. slightly
a tempo, with motion
f

22
p
mf
mp
25
28
a tempo
rit.
p
31
rhythmically, with motion
mf

34
f
37
mp
p
40
pp
43
p

slightly faster

58
mp
p
61
Tempo I
f
64
rit.
67
p
pp

Nice Work If You Can Get It

Music and Lyrics by
George Gershwin and Ira Gershwin
Arranged by Tom Gerou

© 1937 (Renewed) GEORGE GERSHWIN MUSIC and IRA GERSHWIN MUSIC
All Rights Administered by WB MUSIC CORP.
All Rights Reserved

9
Strol - ing with the one girl,
11
Sigh - ing sigh af - ter sigh,
Nice Work If You Can
14
Get It, And you can get it if you try.
16
mp Just im - ag - ine some - one

19
Wait - ing at the cot - tage
door,
21
Where two hearts be - come one
Who could
cresc.
23
ask for an - y - thing more?
25
mf
Lov - ing one who loves you,

27
And then tak - ing that vow,
29
Nice Work If You Can Get It, And if you
31
get it,
f
Won't you tell me
33
how?

The Man I Love

Music and Lyrics by
George Gershwin and Ira Gershwin
Arranged by Tom Gerou

© 1924 (Renewed) WB MUSIC CORP.
All Rights Reserved

9
He'll look at me and smile,
I'll un - der - stand;
mf
11
And in a lit - tle while
He'll take my hand;
13
And though it seems ab - surd,
I know we both won't
15
say a word.

17
May - be I shall meet him
Sun - day, may - be
19
Mon - day, may - be
not;
21
Still I'm sure to meet him
one day, May - be
23
Tues - day will be
my good news day.

25
p
He'll build a lit - tle home,
Just meant for two,
27
From which I'll nev - er roam,
Who would, would you?
29
And so all else a - bove,
I'm wait - ing for the
31
man I
love.
pp

Embraceable You

Music and Lyrics by
George Gershwin and Ira Gershwin
Arranged by Tom Gerou

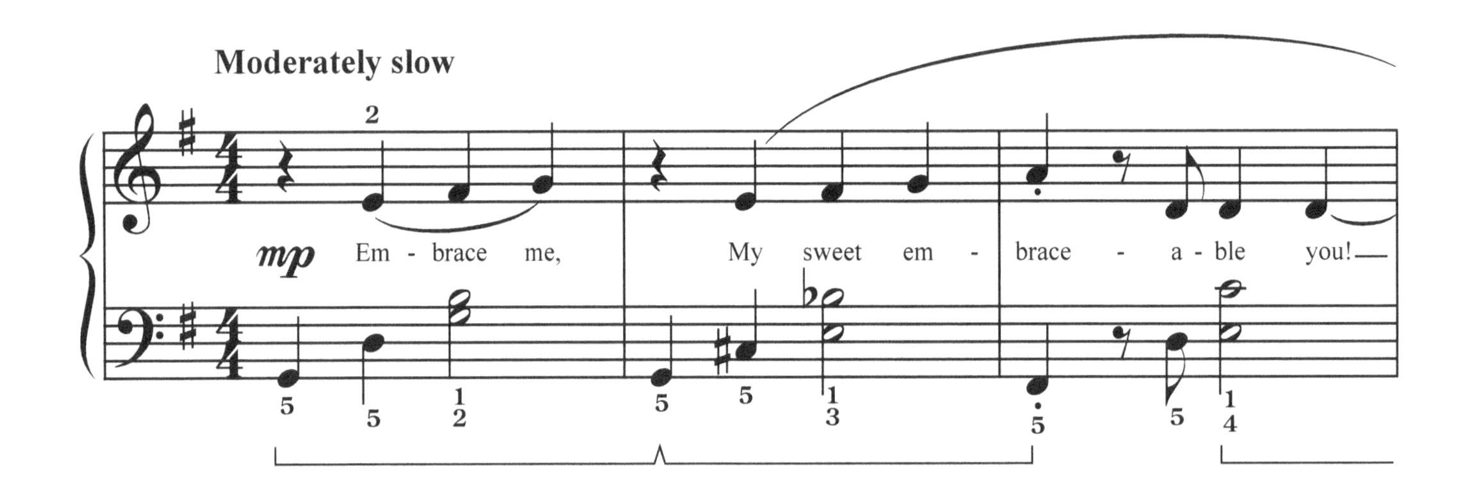

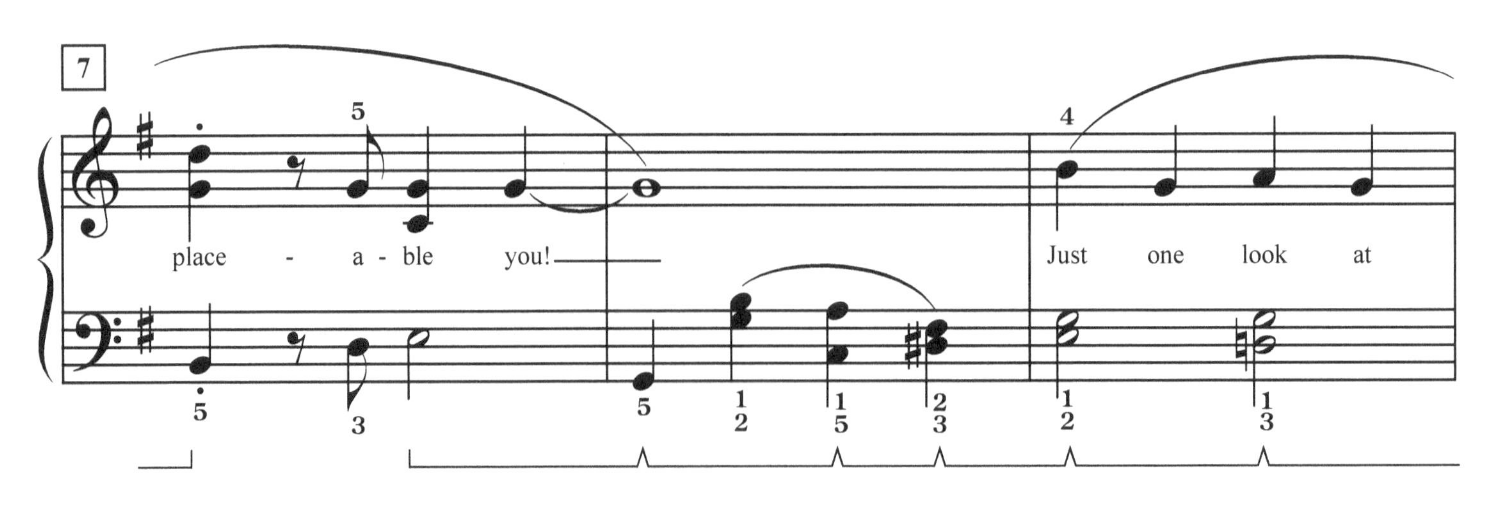

© 1930 (Renewed) WB MUSIC CORP.
All Rights Reserved

10
you, my heart grew tip - sy in me;
13
You and you a - lone bring out the gyp - sy in me!
cresc.
mf
16
mp
I love all the man - y
19
charms a - bout you;
A - bove all

22
I want my arms a - bout you.
25
Don't be a naught - y ba - by,
Come to pa - pa, Come to
mf
cresc.
28
pa - pa, do!
My sweet em - brace - a - ble
f
31
you!
mf

Someone to Watch over Me

Music and Lyrics by
George Gershwin and Ira Gershwin
Arranged by Tom Gerou

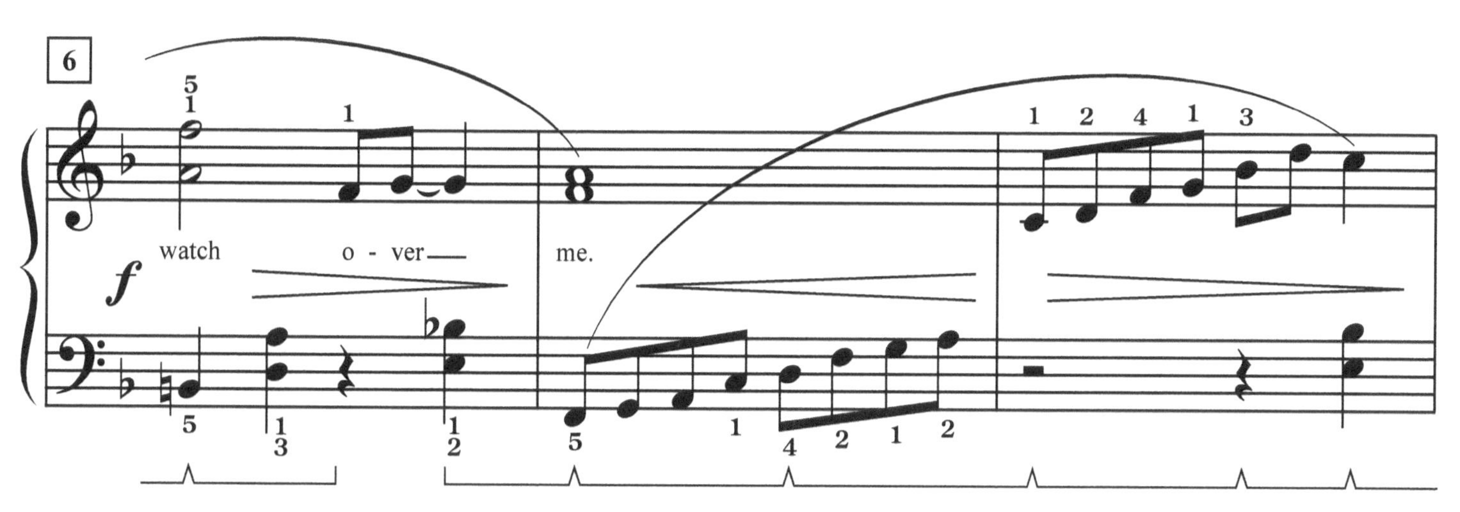

© 1926 (Renewed) WB MUSIC CORP.
All Rights Reserved

9
I'm a lit - tle lamb who's lost in the wood.
I know I could
12
Al - ways be good
To one who'll watch o - ver
15
me.
mp
Al - though he may not be the
18
man some Girls think of as hand - some. To

21
my heart he car - ries the key.
24
mf
Won't you tell him please to put on some speed,
27
Fol - low my lead, Oh, how I need Some - one to
30
f
watch o - ver me.
rit.
p
8va

Summertime

Music and Lyrics by George Gershwin,
Du Bose and Dorothy Heyward and Ira Gershwin
Arranged by Tom Gerou

© 1935 (Renewed) GEORGE GERSHWIN MUSIC, IRA GERSHWIN MUSIC and
DU BOSE AND DOROTHY HEYWARD MEMORIAL FUND
All Rights Administered by WB MUSIC CORP.
All Rights Reserved

9
high.
p
Oh yo'
11
dad - dy's rich, —
an' yo' ma is good - look - in',
14
mf
So hush, lit - tle ba - by,
16
don' — yo'
cry.

19
p
One of these morn - in's
22
You goin' to rise up sing - in',
Then you'll
25
mp
spread yo' wings
mf
an' you'll take to the
27
sky.
p
But till that

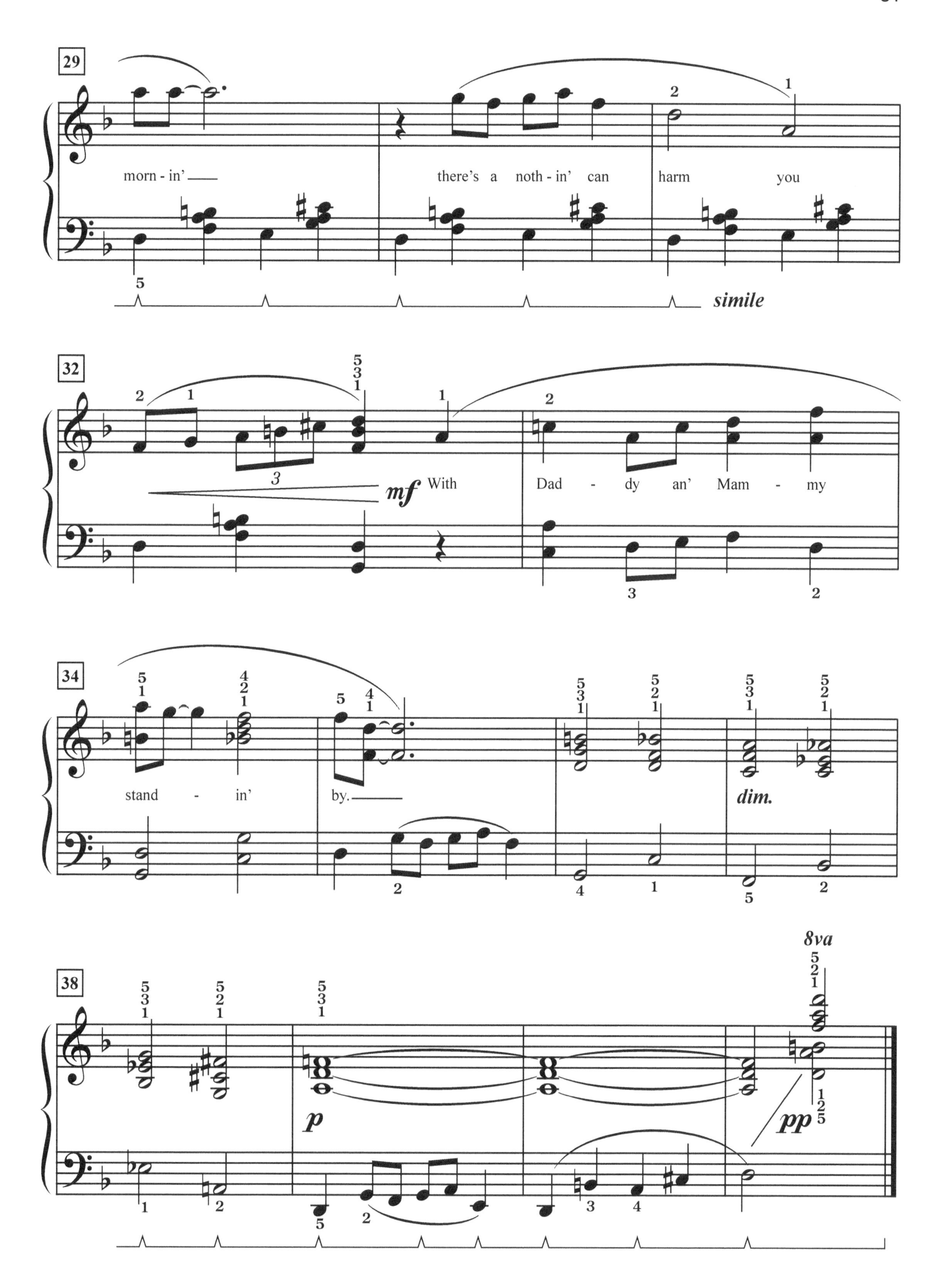
29
morn - in'
there's a noth - in' can
harm you
simile
32
mf With
Dad - dy an' Mam - my
34
stand - in'
by.
dim.
38
p
8va
pp

They Can't Take That Away from Me

Music and Lyrics by
George Gershwin and Ira Gershwin
Arranged by Tom Gerou

© 1936, 1937 (Copyrights Renewed) GEORGE GERSHWIN MUSIC and IRA GERSHWIN MUSIC
All Rights Administered by WB MUSIC CORP.
All Rights Reserved

9
mp
The way your smile just beams,
11
The way you sing off key,
13
The way you haunt my dreams,
15
mf
No, no! They Can't Take That A - way from Me!

17
We may never, never meet again On the
20
bump-y road to love, Still I'll always, always
23
keep the mem-'ry of
The way you hold your knife,
26
The way we danced 'till three,

29
The way you've changed my life.
31
mf
No, no! They Can't Take That A - way from Me!
33
f
No! They Can't Take That A -
35
way from Me!

Strike Up the Band!

Music and Lyrics by
George Gershwin and Ira Gershwin
Arranged by Tom Gerou

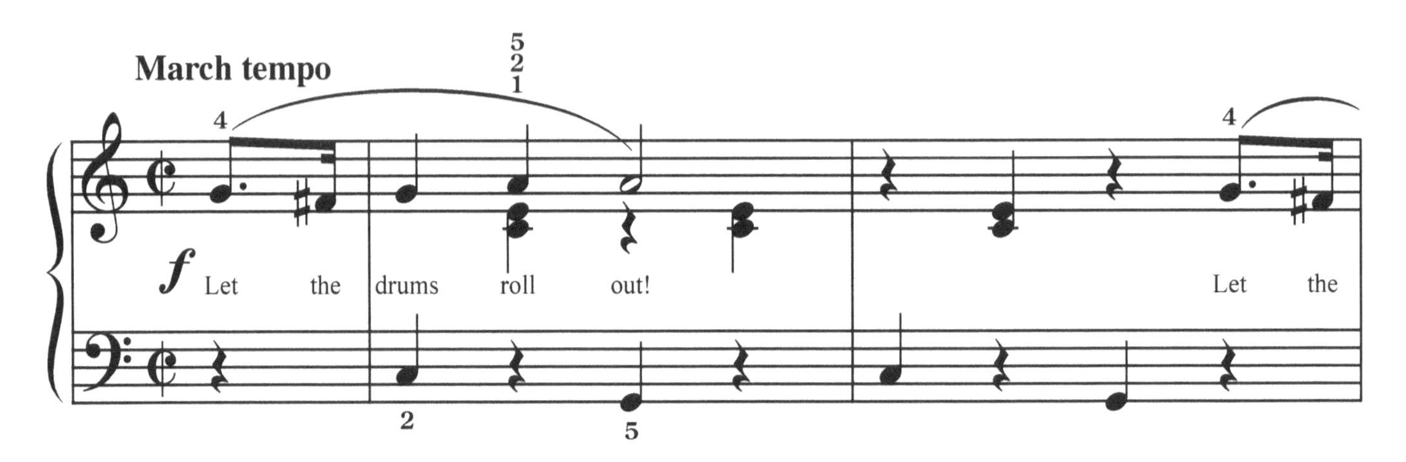

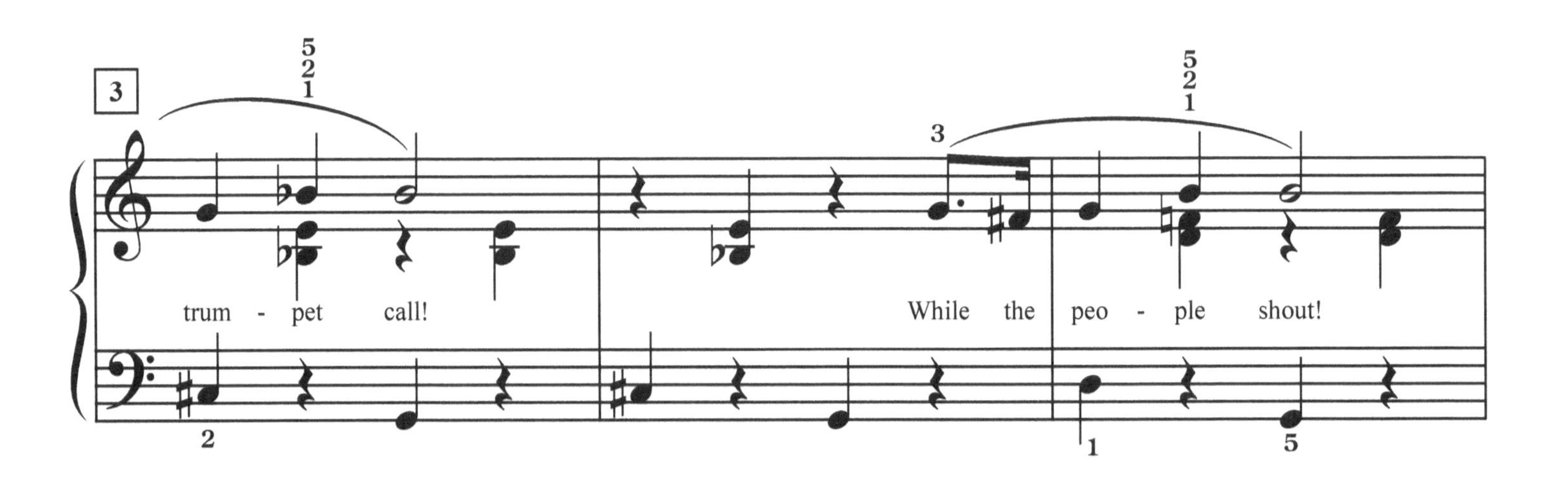

© 1927 (Renewed) WB MUSIC CORP.
All Rights Reserved

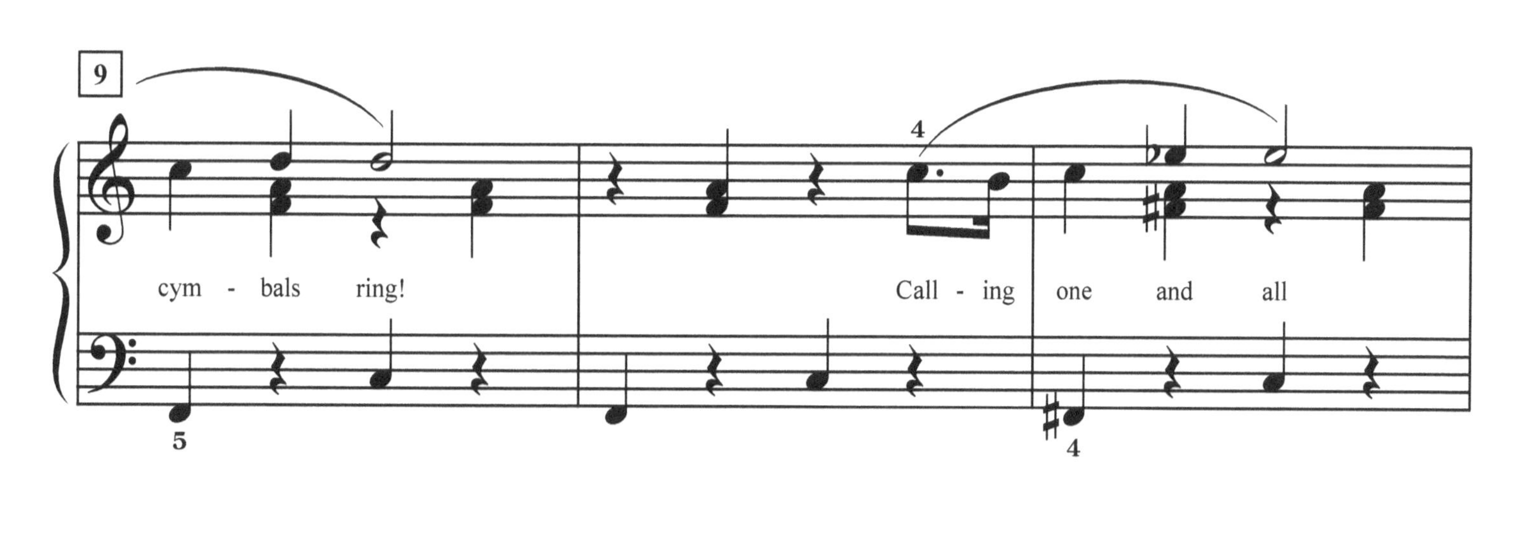
9
cym - bals ring! Call - ing one and all

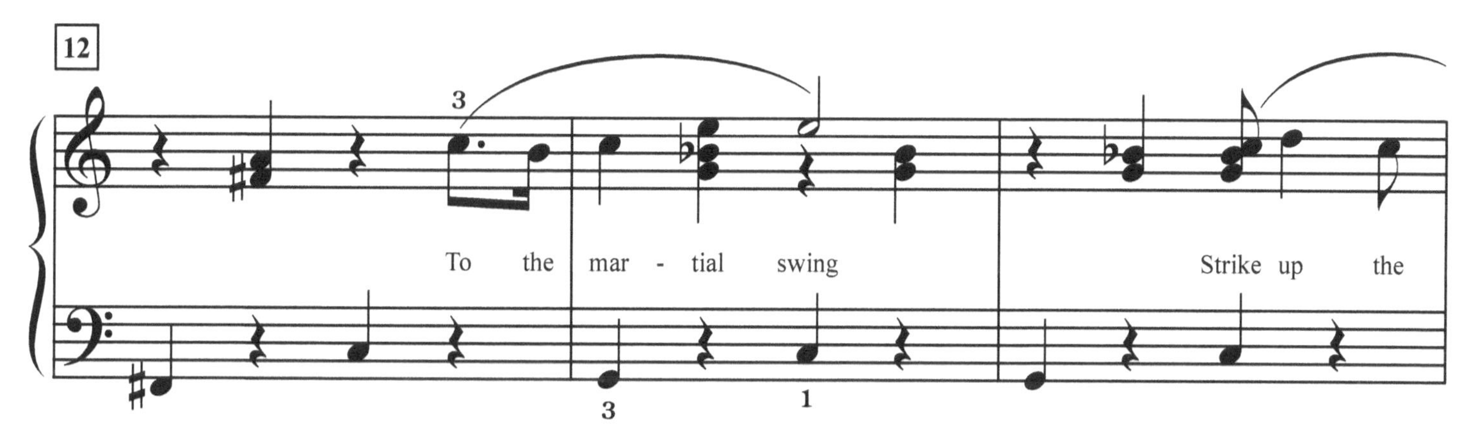
12
To the mar - tial swing Strike up the

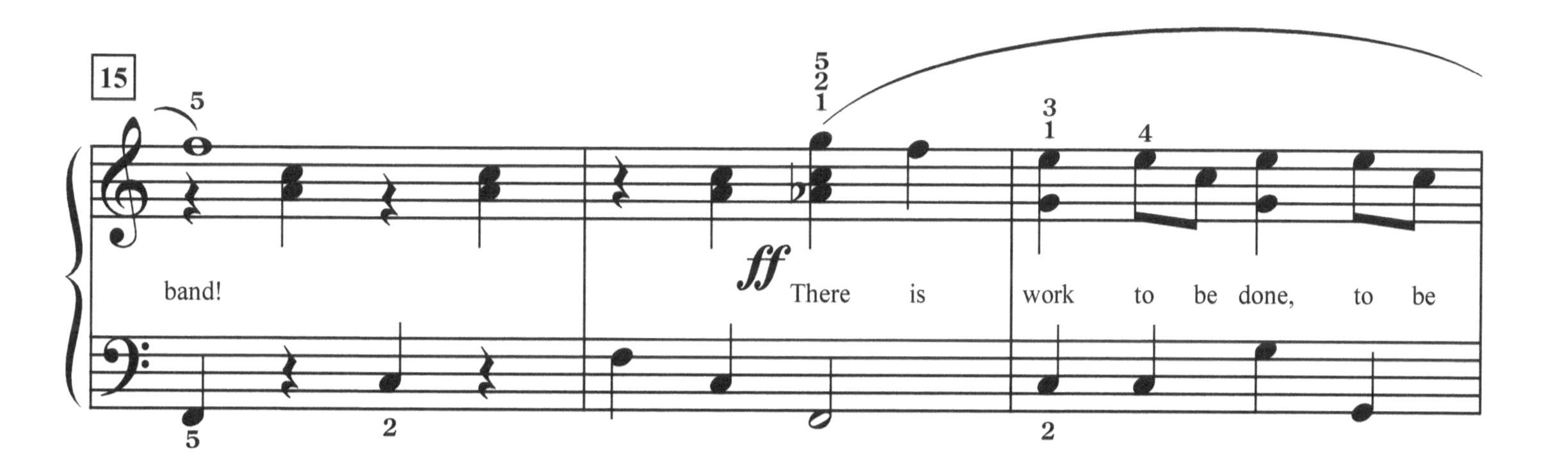
15
band! ff There is work to be done, to be

18
done! There's a war to be won, to be won! Come, you

21
son of a son of a gun! Take your stand!
24
Fall in line, yea bo! Come a-
27
long, let's go! Hey, lead - er!
30
Strike up the band!
ff

Three-Quarter Blues

By George Gershwin
Arranged by Tom Gerou

Moderately slow, with motion

© 1967 (Renewed) CHAPPELL & CO., INC.
All Rights Reserved

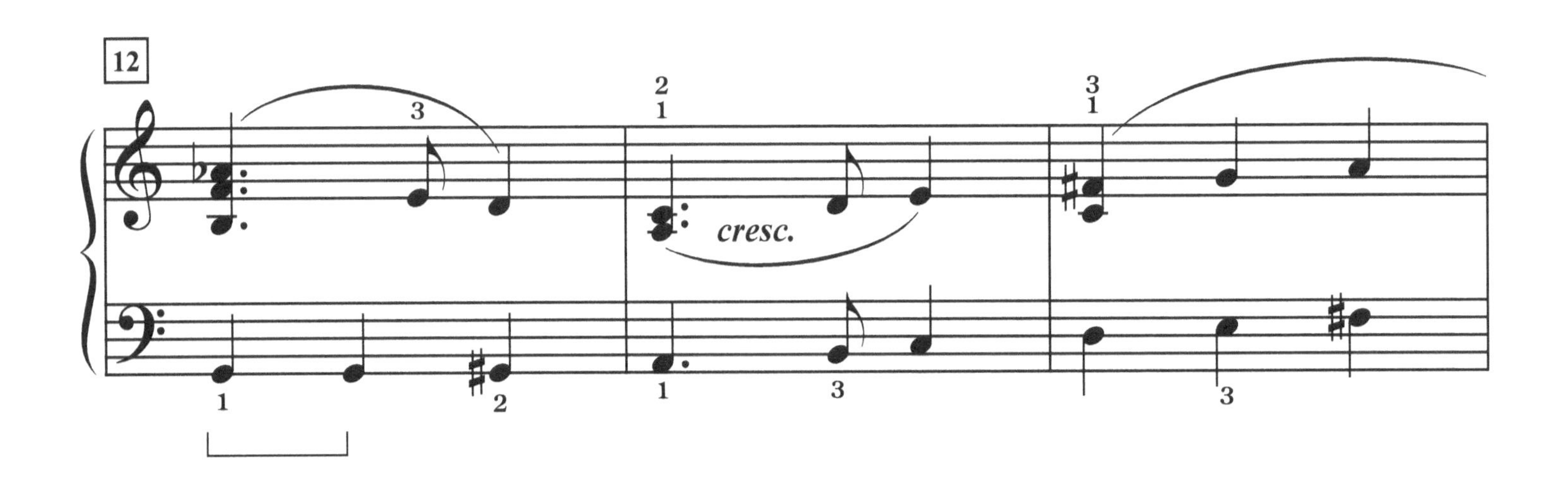
12
cresc.

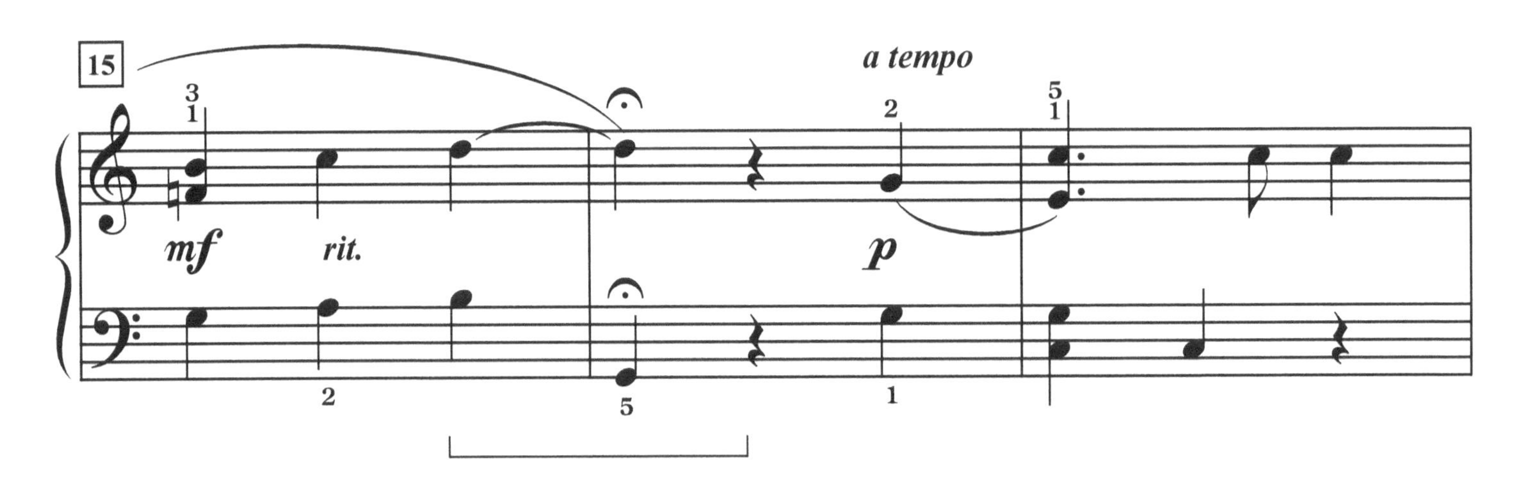
15
a tempo
mf
rit.
p

18

21

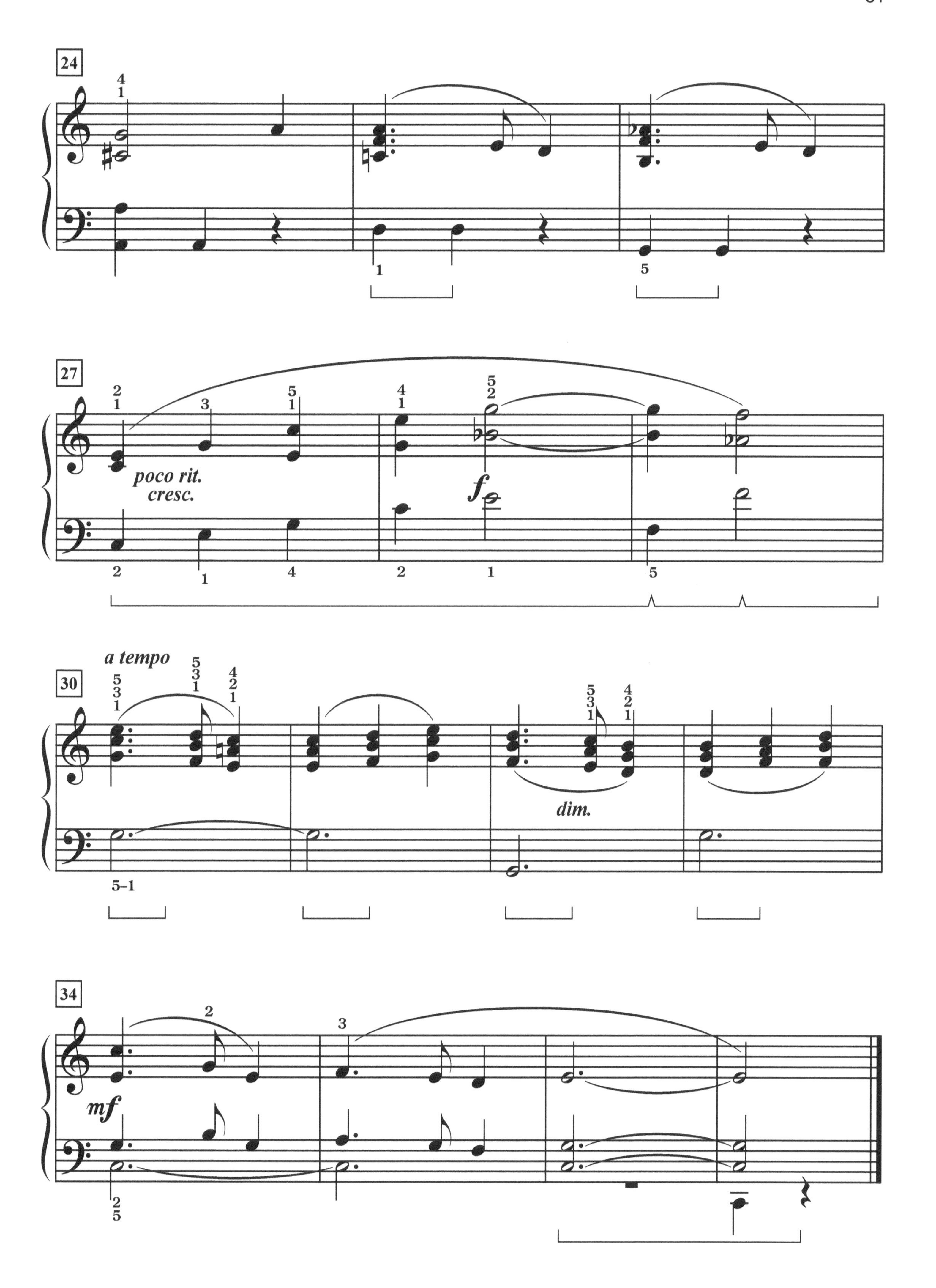
24
27
poco rit.
cresc.
f
30
a tempo
dim.
34
mf

But Not for Me

Music and Lyrics by
George Gershwin and Ira Gershwin
Arranged by Tom Gerou

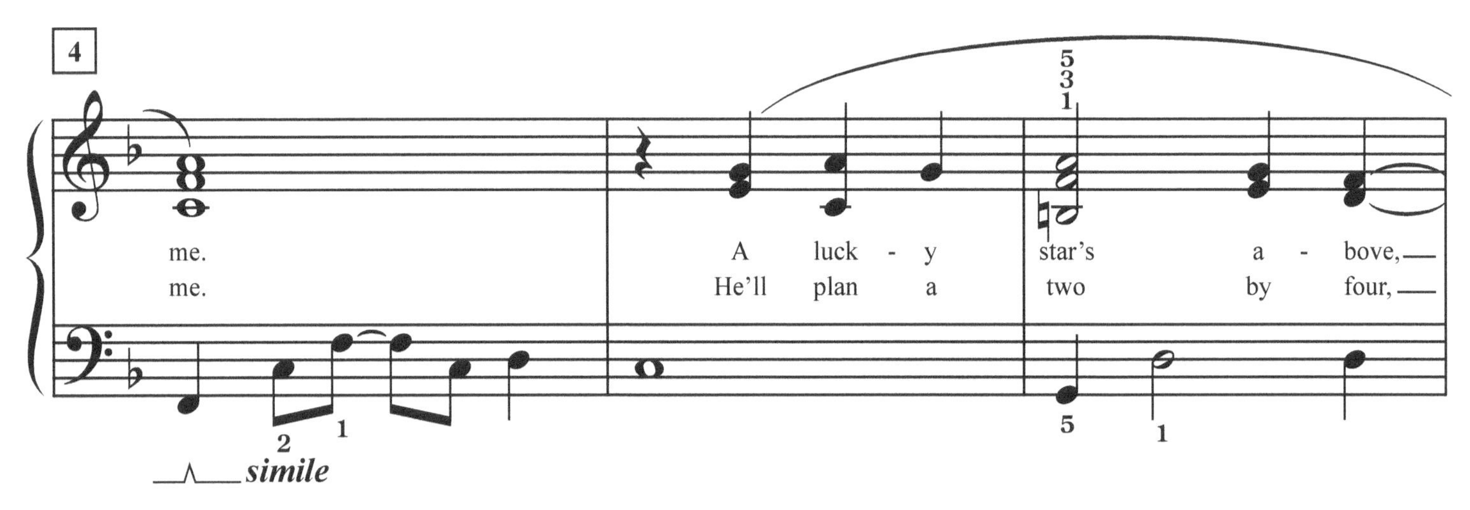

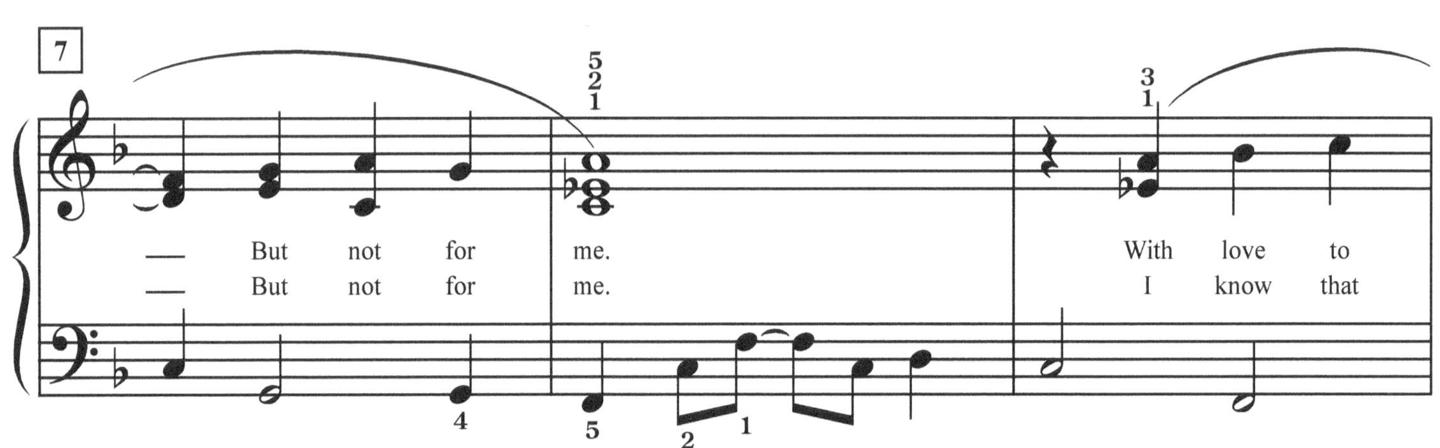

© 1930 (Renewed) WB MUSIC CORP.
All Rights Reserved

10
lead the way I've found more clouds of gray
love's a game; I'm puz - zled, just the same,
13
Than an - y Rus - sian play Could guar - an -
Was I the moth or flame? I'm all at
16
tee. I was a fool to fall
sea. It all be - gan so well,
19
And get that way; Heigh - ho! A -
But what an end! This is the
simile

22
las! and al - so, Lack - a day!
time a fell - er needs a friend,
25
Al - though I can't dis - miss The mem - 'ry
When ev - 'ry hap - py plot Ends with the
28
of his kiss, I guess he's not
mar - riage knot, And there's no knot
31
1.
2.
8va
for me.
for me.
8va

’S Wonderful

Music and Lyrics by
George Gershwin and Ira Gershwin
Arranged by Tom Gerou

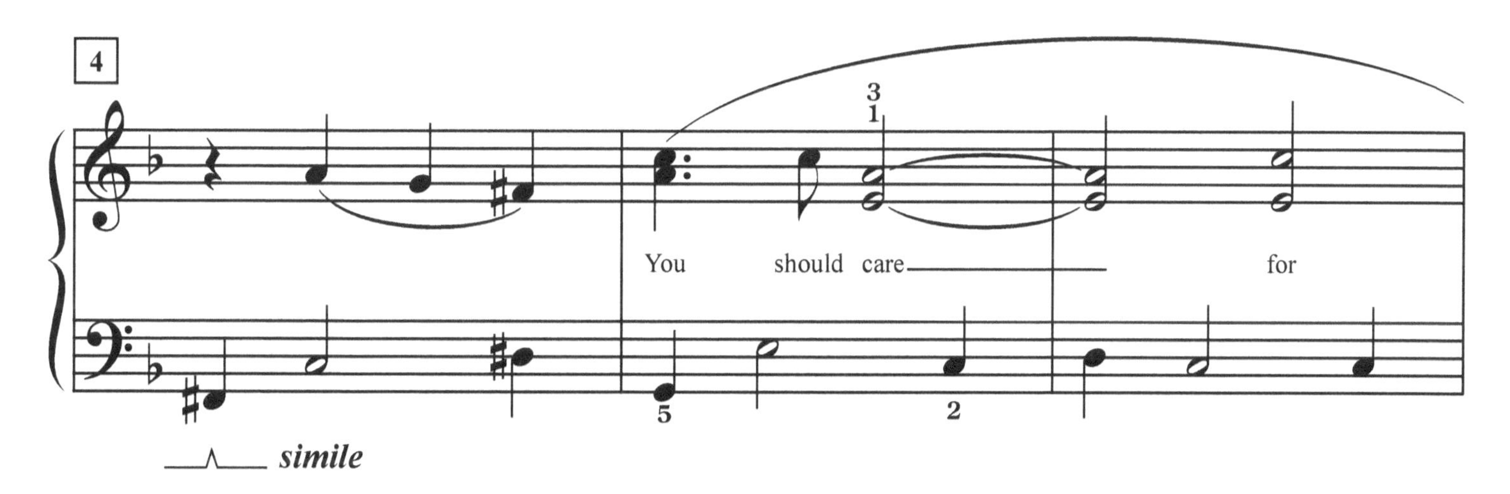

© 1927 (Renewed) WB MUSIC CORP.
All Rights Reserved

10
'S par - a - dise!
13
'S what I love to see!
16
You've made my life so
mf
19
glam - or - ous
You can't blame
simile

22
me for feel - ing am - or - ous.
24
a tempo
Oh!
rit.
'S won - der - ful!
p
27
'S mar - vel - ous!
mf
That you should care
f
30
for me!
rit.

Rhapsody in Blue™

Music by George Gershwin
Arranged by Tom Gerou

© 1924 (Renewed) WB MUSIC CORP.
All Rights Reserved

9
f
11
slightly agitated
mf
dim. e poco rit.
14
16
a tempo
mf

18
Moderately fast
pp
mf
tranquilly
20
23
f
25
Faster
mp
legato

27
30
33
poco rit.
36
a tempo
mf

39
41
44
rit.
a tempo
p tranquilly
46

48
mp
50
Quickly
p
rit.
pp
52
Slower and marked
(2nd time 8va)
p
54
rit. 2nd time

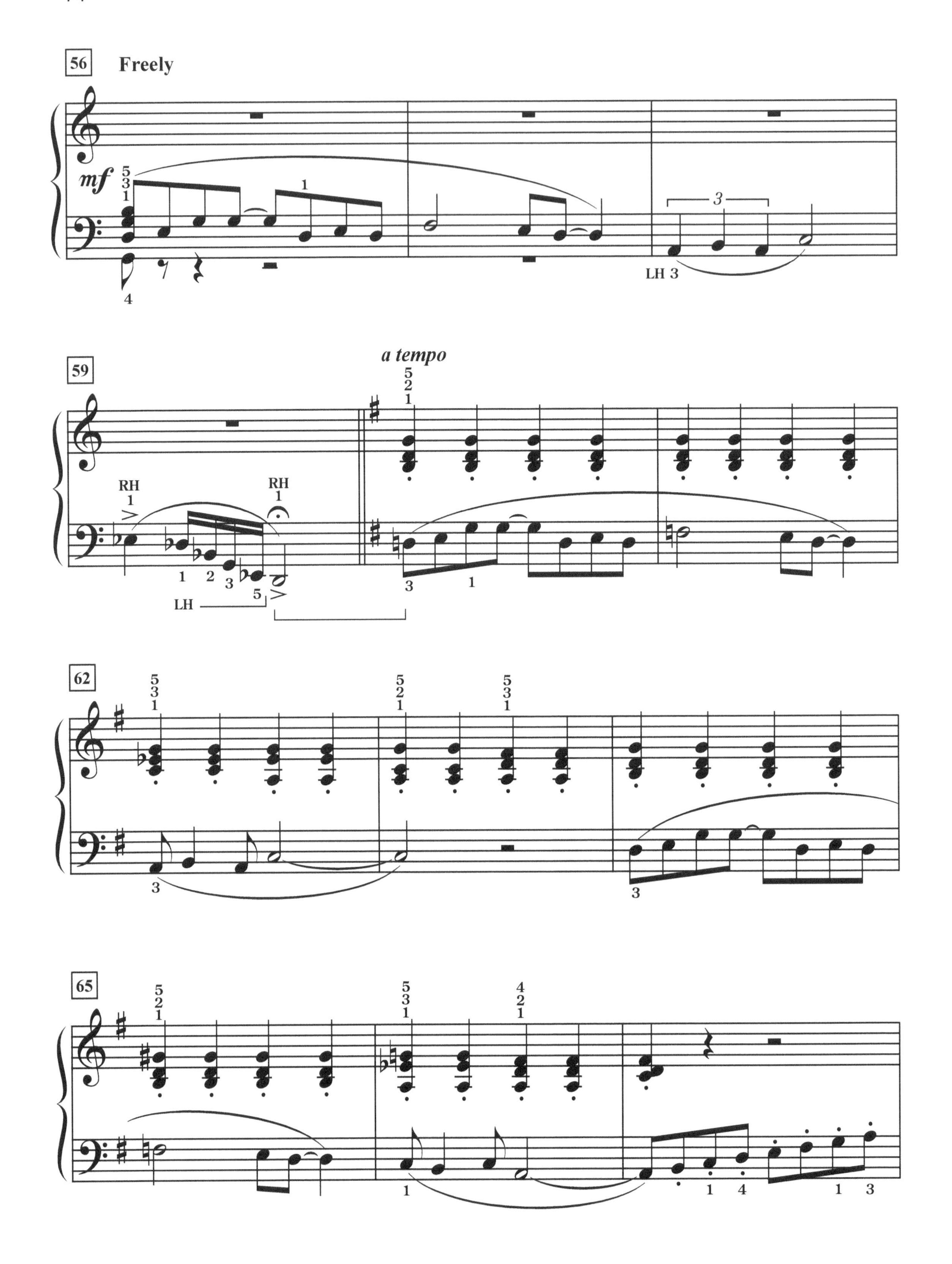
56
Freely
mf
LH 3
59
a tempo
RH
RH
LH
62
65

68

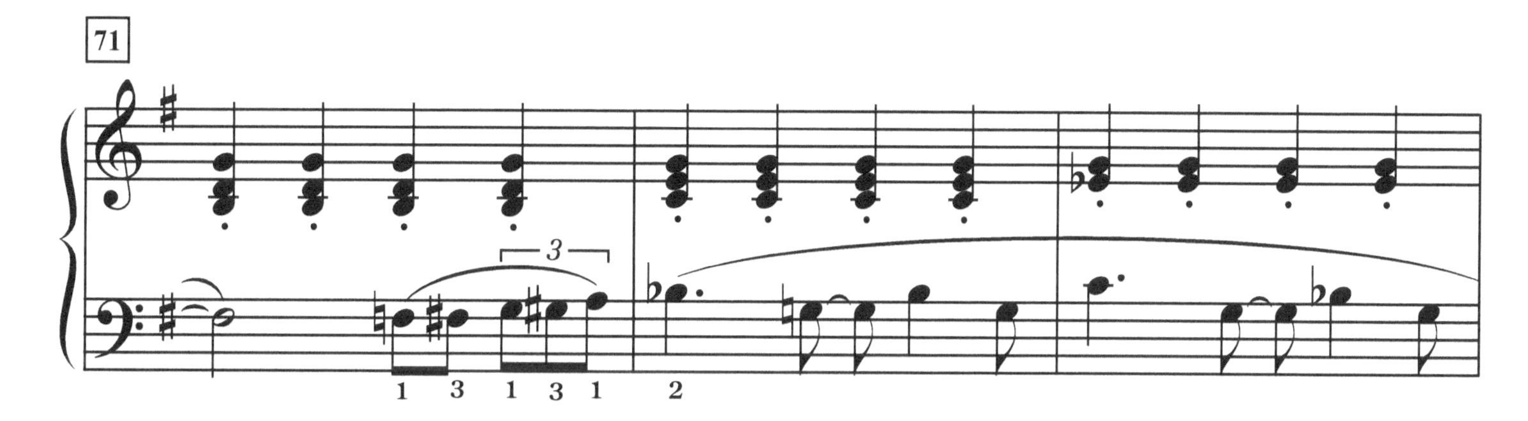
71

74
poco rit.

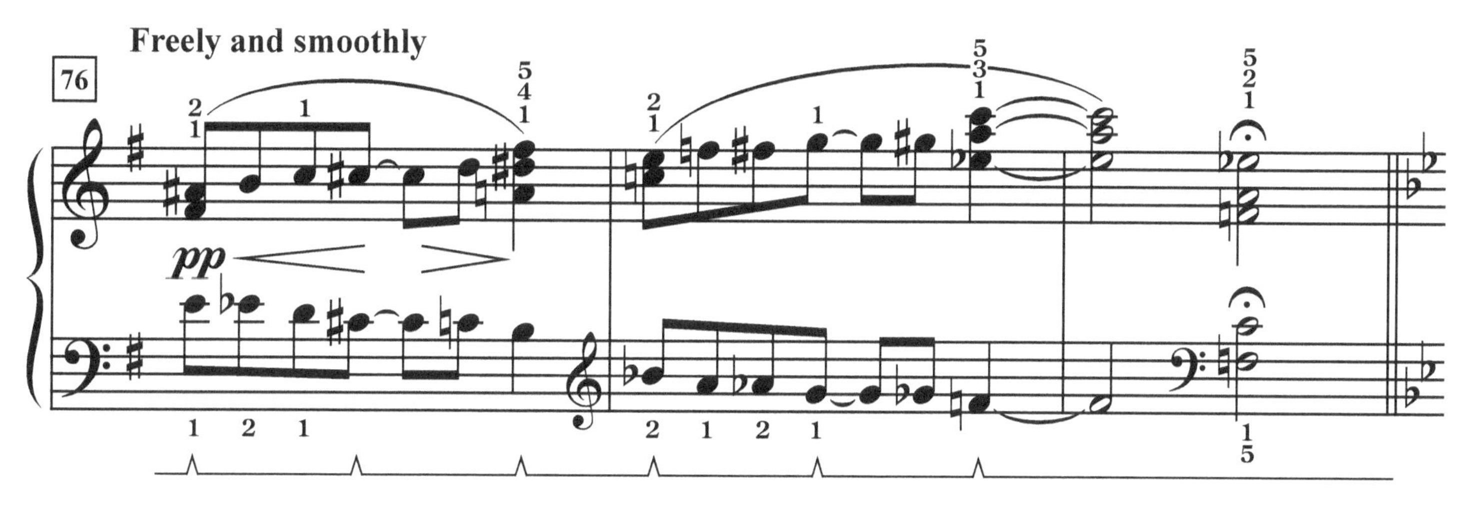
Freely and smoothly
76
pp

Moderately slow, with expression

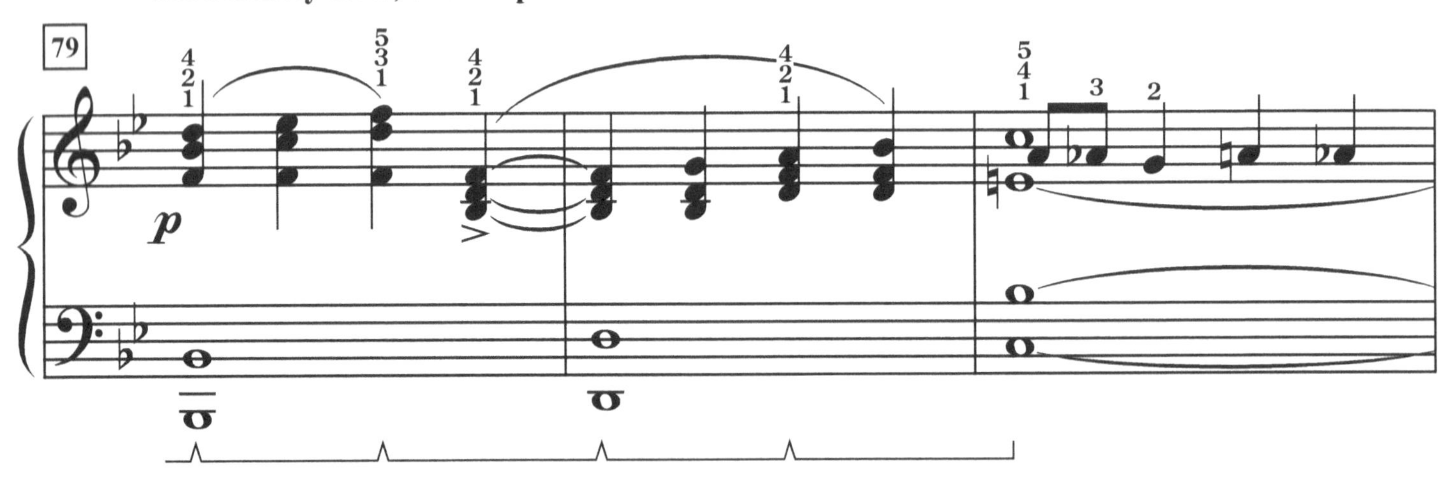

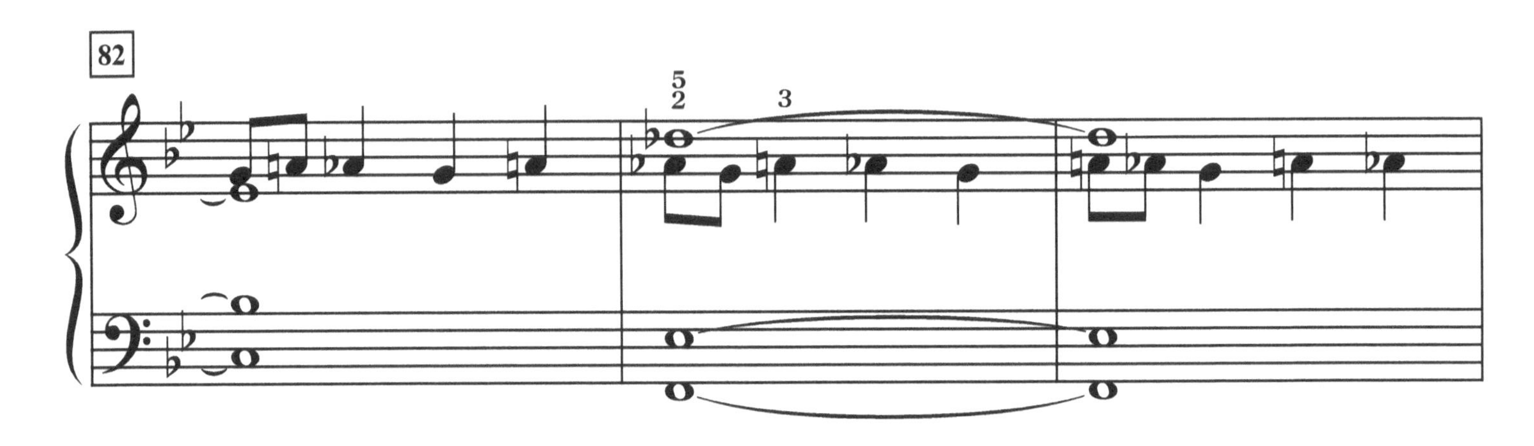

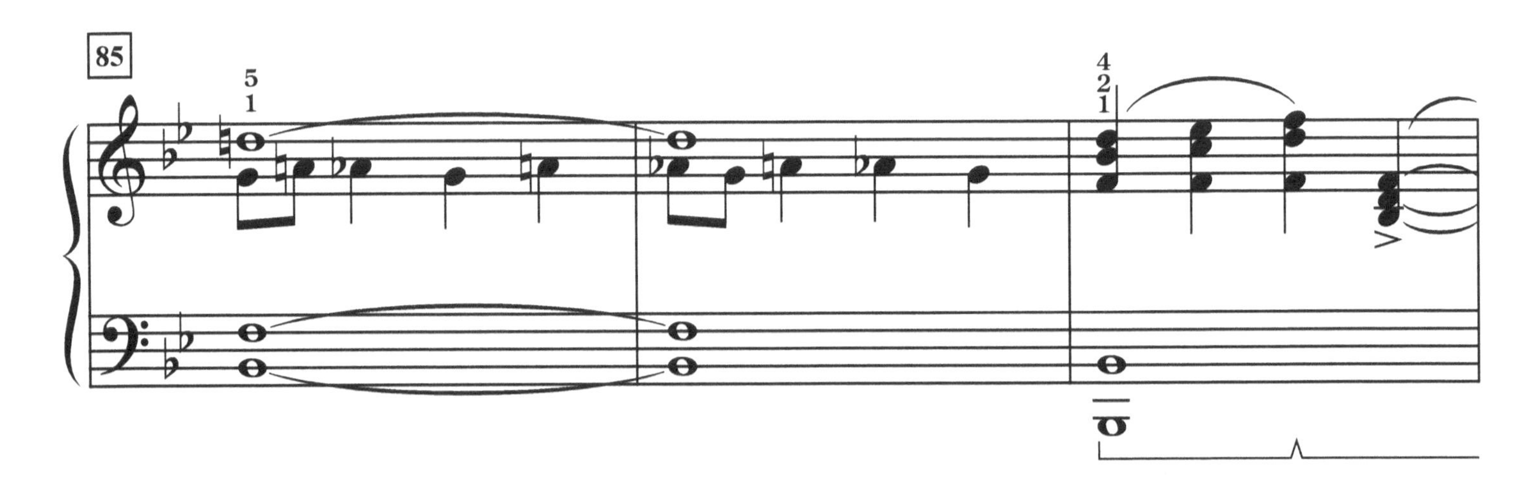

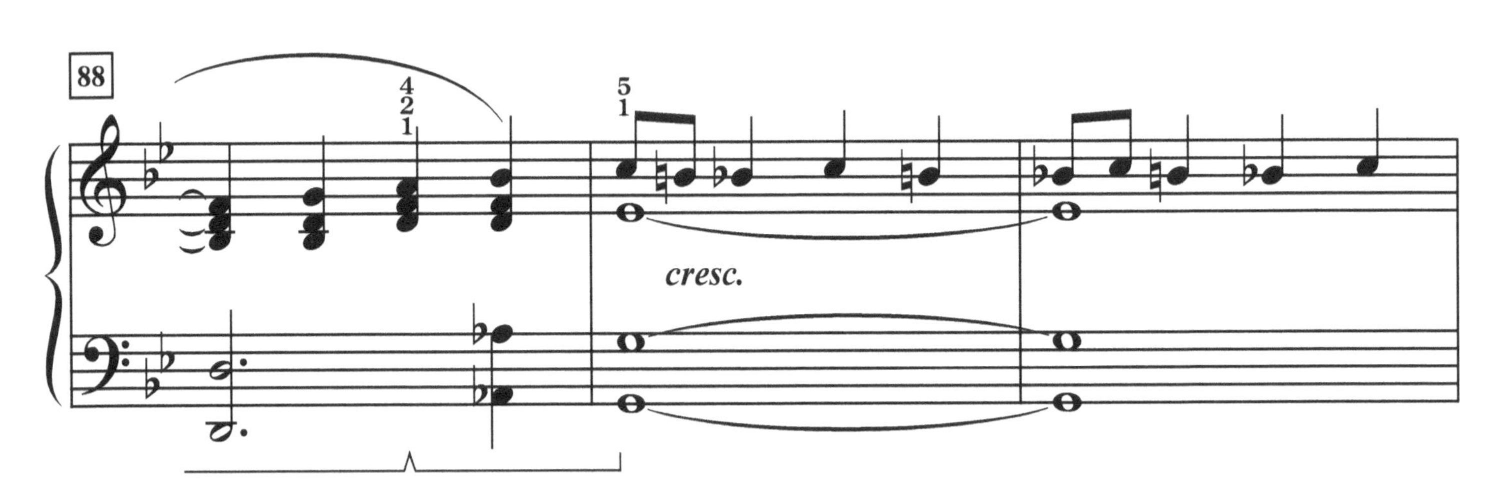

91
mf
94
Freely
mp
98
101
a tempo
f
mf

105
f
mf
8va
109
f
112
116

119
ff
ped. simile
121
123
Broadly
125
poco a poco rit.

Very grand
127
129
131
8va
133
8va